HENRIETTE LANG
AND STU BAKER

THE
MINDSET
TRIANGLE
BOOK

INTRODUCTION

Mastering that inner voice is often a challenge. Lifting the duvet can often feel like a 10-tonne weight. Here at The Mindset Triangle, we are trying to make your life that little bit easier by sticking to three rules.

EXERCISE, SLEEP, HEALTHY EATING

Living life with depression and anxiety isn't easy. Pulling yourself from under the 10-tonne duvet can be tough and just day-to-day tasks can be a pain.

We campaign to end the stigma of mental illness and to raise awareness of what it means to live with it. With one in four people affected by the condition and suicide being the biggest killer of men under the age of forty-five, there is a huge problem to fix. Twelve men take their life every day in the UK and for every one that takes their life, another twenty attempt it. This is a massive problem and we need to be able to talk about it without the stigma blanket over our heads.

Who remembers learning about the fire triangle in their science class at school? For a fire to burn, you need heat, fuel and oxygen. Without one, the fire will extinguish. We work with the same principle for a healthy mindset.

It may seem silly living your life according to a triangle, but it works. It's so simple to follow and stick up around the house, whether on the beer fridge or in the drawer that holds all the take-away menus. It gives you that chance to change your mind and your actions. We find it useful to reflect on why we feel like we do. If the 10-tonne duvet has got hold of you one morning and won't let me up, look at the three elements.

EXERCISE, SLEEP, HEALTHY EATING.

Nine out of ten times, you will hit the nail on the head within a few seconds and know where to make changes.

This book is to be used as a guide to living a healthier lifestyle for a healthier mindset. Feel free to grab a pen and make a recipe of your own. Be inventive and have fun. Take away hints and tips from all our interviewees on their experiences of living with mental illness and enjoy a workout designed by Stu for an effective, easy, twenty-minute all-body blast.

Enjoy the book and make it your own!

Chilli Sauce

1 can of tomatoes

1 tbsp tomato puree

Chilli, chopped (the amount is up to you)

1 small onion, peeled and roughly chopped

2 cloves of garlic, peeled and sliced

1 tbsp white wine vinegar

1 pinch of salt to taste

Method

1. Bung all of the ingredients into a blender and whiz together.
2. Done! This recipe is perfect for dips or pasta sauces.

Eggs Baked in a Tomato

6 tomatoes
Glug of oil
Twist of salt and pepper
Small handful of spinach, chopped
6 medium eggs
2 Cloves of garlic,
finely chopped

Method

1. Preheat oven to 200°C. While that's getting warm, cut the tops off the tomatoes and scoop out the insides. Then, bung in a muffin tray.
2. Drizzle a glug of oil in each tomato and bung in the garlic. Throw in the oven for 15 minutes.
3. Once out, stick in the spinach and crack in an egg. Throw back in the oven for another 15 minutes.
4. Great for a lunchbox!

PREP

One of the most **EFFECTIVE** full-body exercises around, a burpee starts out in a low **SQUAT** position with your hands on the floor. Next, **KICK** your feet back to a **PUSH-UP** position, complete one push-up, then immediately return your feet to the squat position. Leap up as high as possible before **SQUATTING** and moving back into the push-up portion of the show.

BURPEES

Starting on your hands and knees, bring your left foot forward directly under your chest while straightening your right leg. Keeping your hands on the ground and your core tight, jump and switch legs. Your left leg should now be extended behind your body with your right knee forward. Next up? Everest!

CARDIO VASCULAR

SPEED SKATING

Find your inner Olympian. Staying in a low position, explode off one leg to another while swinging your arms. Land on each leg with a squat and explode again. It will be no time before you're picked up and put on the ice!

CARDIO VASCULAR

Hope Virgo

Mental Health Campaigner
and Author

WHAT IS YOUR EXPERIENCE WITH MENTAL ILLNESS?

I had anorexia from when I was 12 or 13 years old, but was officially diagnosed when I was sixteen. When I was thirteen, I was sexually abused and had a messy family life. My way of coping was to stop eating and to exercise all the time. I managed to hide it from everyone.

When I was sixteen, my school intervened and my mum got involved. I then spent a year going to a child adolescence mental health service in Bristol. This didn't work for me; I was very unwell and couldn't hide it anymore. My lowest weight was 40 kilograms. I ended up getting admitted into hospital because my heart was in a critical condition. I was so critical, in fact, that my internal organs were damaged because of the anorexia.

I spent a year in intensive therapy in hospital. I was with ten other girls and one boy. I had talking therapy, and was taught how to eat again and how to exercise in a healthy way. I was discharged at the age of eighteen and have been managing my recovery ever since. I am now twenty-seven years old.

WHAT DO YOU DO TO KEEP YOURSELF ON A STEADY LEVEL?

I eat very healthy small meals regularly throughout the day. I also exercise well – not too much and not too little. I used to get obsessed with exercise, but now I have a personal trainer who is teaching me how to exercise in a healthy way.

WHAT IS YOUR FAVOURITE FOOD?

I love Lebanese food, kebabs, houmous and flat bread.

RAOK

Leave money in a vending machine

Take your shopping trolley inside

Pay for food at a drive-through
for the person behind you

Deliver cakes to a friend

Say thank you

Smile

Buy a dozen flowers and hand them
out to people

Pick up litter in a public place

Donate toys or books to a charity
organisation

Leave a nice tip for your waiter
or waitress

Do something nice for another
family member

Have your kids draw a picture
for someone and take it to them

RAOK

Compliment your child's schoolteacher by writing them a note or making a phone call

Call a neighbour and ask if they need anything from the store

Give another family member a back scratch or a foot rub

Write encouraging and uplifting notes and leave them around the house in random places

Be nice

Give a sincere compliment to five people

Take flowers to those living in an old peoples home

Leave a treat on a neighbours doorstep anonymously

Donate blood

Stu Baker

Founder of The Mindset Triangle,
Personal Trainer,
Mental health advocate and author

WHAT IS YOUR EXPERIENCE WITH MENTAL ILLNESS?

I reckon I have had depression and anxiety for most of my adult life starting back in 2000. There is evidence to suggest that a tablet I took from when I was in the Royal Navy for anti-malaria is to blame, but it is very hard to get that conviction. To be fair I have had come to accept what I have and it doesn't or won't make it any better with someone or something to blame. During my 20's and being in the Navy, my life was more or less based around drinking and playing rugby, so I believe these together masked a lot of my illness. There were times that I self-harmed and had suicidal thoughts, but just thought it was normal. By the time I was 27 I had 2 fail relationships with 3 kids and living back with my mum in Coventry. It wasn't until I had a bad injury whilst playing rugby and had to retire from the game that I noticed my mental health had dramatically slid downhill. Socialising and drinking was on the rise.

A few years had passed, and I was living in Birmingham with my new partner and it was noticeable that I couldn't hold a job down. Every day it was harder to get out of bed and the general day to day tasks were a ball ache. I was reluctantly dragged to the doctors for me to lay it all out about how I wanted to take my own life and was self-harming and felt awful. The doctors response was: "I just think you need to cheer up". I stormed out of the surgery and headed home not having a clue what to do. I thought that was it and there was no hope. A week later I was convinced to go to the doctors again and thankfully this doctor was ace. She prescribed me tablets and put me forward for therapy. Years passed I got married, good job and had regular contact with the kids. I still didn't talk about my mental health because of male pride but I started blog, which I felt was a great help. During this time I came up with concept of The Mindset Triangle.

I never thought that I would be here 5 years later writing a book. Its not a cure for my illness as last year has shown. My marriage failed, I wrote this book, work was really tough in the gym to find clients and I started to write my life story bringing a lot of stuff up that I had hid from when I was a child. The worst thing was that I did, was not speak about it, but I honestly thought I was fine until 10th November, when I needed air and walked out the house.

4 pubs later I found myself on a bridge being detained by the police after wanting to take my own life. I voluntarily admitted myself into an acute mental health unit for 7 days in Birmingham to strip back and start again.

Now I am in a much better place and talk about everything. Good or Bad. I fully expect to have bad days again and will do for the rest of my life but I am confident I can keep on track and NEVER return to that bridge.

WHAT DO YOU DO TO KEEP YOURSELF ON A STEADY LEVEL?

Stick to the triangle. Some days are better than others, but I try my best. Talking is key. My daughter who I live with Charlotte is a massive help and Henriette, the other half of the book. The amount of time I spend with them and talk to them openly they can see my 'twitches' or 'ticks' before I do and ask questions. Before I was embarrassed, annoyed and felt weak if they noticed but now its cool. They would ask questions if I walked in the door with a black eye so what's the difference with my mental state. So yeah, the two T's... Talk and triangle.

WHAT IS YOUR FAVOURITE FOOD?

I probably could have answered that really easily before I started writing this book but now I have about 40. I know it's a bit of a cliché and a cop out but the recipes in the book are favourite as they have been shortlisted from the 100's that we wrote. Chicken bombs are amazing, I'm forever eating dirty rice because of the convenience and ham baskets are always in the fridge because I love a snack. Has that answered the question? Lol

Stu became very close to Terry at an acute mental health unit towards the end of 2017 where he was staying. Terry is a former soldier and now lives with PTSD. He finds calmness and tranquillity in writing poetry. One morning over breakfast Terry presented Stu with this poem. We think it speaks volumes.

Do You Know Me?

Hi, do you know me?
I'm the man that says nothing yet,
I live with mental illness.
Where some go, speak, cry and let the doctor treat,
Others walk around dead on their feet.
They don't sleep, hardly eat and, for sure, never exercise.
I've met a lot of people in and out of mental illness,
But none who have the concept to treat,
Don't get it wrong, this is no cure,
But may keep the psychiatrist from the door.
Don't stay quiet, don't be ashamed, let's fight against it,
Learn to like yourself again, tell the world,
I live with mental illness,
So, don't give up, this road isn't over.

Terence Griffiths.

TWO-SECOND SPRINT

AND

TWO SQUAT JUMPS

SPRINT AS FAST AS YOU CAN ON THE SPOT FOR TWO SECONDS, THEN PERFORM TWO SQUAT JUMPS AS THOUGH YOU'RE JUMPING OVER HURDLES. AS SOON AS YOU LAND, IT'S TIME TO SPRINT AGAIN

TUCK JUMP

STANDING WITH YOUR KNEES SLIGHTLY BENT, JUMP AS HIGH AS POSSIBLE AND BRING YOUR KNEES IN TOWARDS YOUR CHEST WHILE EXTENDING YOUR ARMS OUT STRAIGHT. LAND WITH YOUR KNEES SLIGHTLY BENT AND QUICKLY JUMP AGAIN.

CARDIO VASCULAR

Method

1. Grab a muffin tray and lightly oil the cups.
2. Line each cup with a slice of ham. In the base of the pocket, throw in 2–3 leaves of spinach and a pinch of spring onion.
3. Crack an egg in each pocket and add a twist of pepper on each egg.
4. Place the muffin tray on the top shelf of a preheated oven at 200ºC. Cook for 10–12 minutes until the egg is cooked, but still has a slight bounce.

- 6 eggs
- 1 handful of spinach
- 6 slices of ham
- 1 spring onion, chopped

PREP

eggs in ham baskets

- A massive handful of basil leaves
- ½ large avocado
- 2 cloves of garlic
- Good handful of spinach
- 1 squeeze of lemon juice
- 3 tbsp water, more if necessary
- Good handful of parmesan cheese, grated
- Twist of salt

Method

1. Bung everything into a blender except the water and pulse. Then, add the water a little at a time to find your desired consistency.
2. Throw into a pot and stick in the fridge to add to pasta or to top a chicken breast. The choice is yours!

pesto

PREP

Jake Tyler

Mental Health Advocate

WHAT IS YOUR EXPERIENCE WITH MENTAL ILLNESS?

I have lived with depression since I was around seventeen years old. I didn't know that I was depressed and it got very bad before I knew what was happening. In the last year and half, I have addressed my depression and tried to recover by living with it and managing it.

I don't know the origins of my depression and wished that it was like an exact science. I think that this is why people feel so lonely with depression, especially if you haven't talked about it, as it is unexplainable and subjective. It is a feeling inside you. I feel I haven't lived in a way that has helped with my depression. I haven't looked after myself and I self medicated. It is an uphill struggle most of the time and I given up on there ever being a cure. I presume that depression is something that I will have to manage for the rest of my life and, in a strange way, accepting this feels like a weight off my shoulders. I have come to terms with the fact that depression will pop up from time to time. I also now know that there are other people going through the same thing.

The point where I knew I needed help was while working in hospitality and running bars. I was taking drugs and living life dangerously in order to take the edge off. I used quick fixes rather than looking after myself in the long term. I drank every day and had a cocaine habit. All of these things acted as a cover up instead of providing a permanent fix. I wanted to let go of that side of my life and is now trying to live a more balanced life.

WHAT DO YOU DO TO KEEP YOURSELF ON A STEADY LEVEL?

I run, walk and speak often about my depression. I read Reasons To Stay Alive by Matt Haig, in which Haig lists the things that make him want to stay alive. I also did this and it made me feel a sense of worth. The hole you fall into when you have a depressive episode is a black void of nothing and doing little things for yourself makes the hole a little bit more bearable to be in. Running and talking everyday helps me, as does being part of a supportive network and trying not to let the depression overtake me.

WHAT IS YOUR FAVOURITE FOOD?

My favourite food has to be Thai – a good, nourishing, comforting kind of food!

On the top:

- 70g blueberries
- 45g oats
- 50g almonds and hazelnuts
- 50g seeds
- 1 tbsp honey
- 50ml almond milk

On the bottom:

- 1 large beetroot, cooked and peeled
- 3 bananas
- 175g oats
- 3 tbsp maple syrup or honey
- 100g hazelnuts and almonds

Method

1. Preheat the oven to 180°C.
2. In a blender or food processor, blitz the ingredients in the 'On the bottom' list. Do the banana and the beetroot first, then the rest of the bits one at a time. You want the mixture to be a bit lumpy.
3. Line a baking sheet with greaseproof paper and spread the mixture in the tin. Bake for 8 minutes, then take it out and place on the side.
4. In a bowl, bung in the ingredients from the 'On the top' list and spread evenly over the 'On the bottom' mixture. Bung back in the oven for another 12–15 minutes until golden. Take out and leave to cool. Enjoy these bad boys!

Energy Bars

Noodle Jars

- A mason jar
- A packet of fresh or cooked noodles
- 1 handful of mixed vegetables, chopped up (I used kale, carrot, peas and mangetout, but anything you have in the fridge is fine)
- 1 handful of leftover cooked chicken
- ½ a handful of bean sprouts
- 1 spring onion
- ½ a handful of fresh coriander
- 1 dollop of curry paste

Method

1. Layer the ingredients into the mason jar. I usually do the noodles and then the chicken, vegetables, spring onion, bean sprouts and, finally, the fresh herbs.
2. Put the lid of the jar on and throw in your work bag.
3. At lunchtime, take the jar out of your bag open lid,... boil kettle pour in water, close lid, shake to mix, open the lid, arm yourself with some eating irons and tuck in!

Spicy Nuts

PREP

- 1 handful of cashew nuts
- 1 handful of macadamia nuts
- 1 handful of whole almonds
- 1 handful of pumpkin seeds
- 1 handful of sunflower seeds
- 3 tbsp sunflower oil
- 2 tbsp honey
- 2 sprigs rosemary, leaves picked
- Good twist of salt and pepper
- 2 tsp cayenne

Method
1. Preheat oven to 180ºC.
2. Bung everything in a bowl and mix. Then, throw in the oven for 15 minutes until the nuts have turned darker. Leave them on a tray to cool, giving them a shake every now and again.
3. Enjoy a film with your snack!

Supt Sean Russell

West Midlands Police
Health Lead

WHAT IS YOUR EXPERIENCE WITH MENTAL ILLNESS?

I am a policeman and have been in the service for twenty-four years with the West Midlands Police. I have seen many people who have been very unwell in my service. I support the police service to ensure that people, both internally and externally, stay well, and if they do become unwell, I ensure that the service treats them properly with respect and dignity. My most proud moment was setting up the Street Triage programme, in which police officers, mental health nurses and ambulance paramedics respond to people in crisis in a joined-up way.

I started my working life in the Royal Navy as a medic and saw the impact of PTSD very early on. I saw the service men returning from the first Gulf War and the challenges it posed to them, the service and the wider community. The lifestyle in the Royal Navy is one of structure and as soon as that structure comes away, there is a challenge as to how to live your life day-to-day. From being in the navy myself, I got a real sense of how easy it is to get onto that slippery slope. It can happen to anyone at any time. My early experiences in mental health made me think of how I could stop people getting onto that slope and how to stop myself, too.

In most of my service, I have been involved in operational jobs or have led investigations. I spent a significant part of my career in Child and Adult Protection, leading a number of high-profile child deaths. My dad was a cop and my mum was a social worker, so I was brought up with my parents supporting vulnerable children through their work. With this kind of work, you start to think about your own resilience and the people around you and, most importantly, how not to take it home with you. I started to think about what would help me and one of these was to build exercise into my daily life. I'm not a marathon geek, but I cycle and keep fit. I don't drink alcohol. I also have a great passion for food. I tour the best restaurants with my wife and children. My therapy is cooking. Cooking takes me into a therapeutic zone; the kitchen is mine and I can relax with food and share what I have created.

WHAT DO YOU DO TO KEEP YOURSELF ON A STEADY LEVEL?

Cooking and exercise. My work is very busy and involves hectic hours. It can often take control over my free time. Cooking makes me feel in control. I can create lovely meals and feel relaxed at the same time.

I also got myself a Brompton fold-up bike, so that I can cycle back and forth to work and in between meetings. It gives me headspace and time for myself in my busy schedule. I can cycle from one meeting to another and think about things, while taking in the delightful views of Birmingham's canals and parks.

WHAT IS YOUR FAVOURITE FOOD?

Guan prawn curry, cooked entirely from scratch.

TOMATO SAUCE

METHOD

1. BUNG TOMATOES, GARLIC AND ONION ONTO A BAKING TRAY AND THROW THEM IN AN OVEN THAT HAS BEEN PREHEATED TO 200°C.
2. AFTER 45 MINUTES, THE VEGETABLES SHOULD BE LOVELY AND CARAMELISED. POUR THE CONTENTS INTO A BLENDER WITH THE BASIL, SALT AND PEPPER. THEN, WHIZ UP!
3. USE THE MIXTURE FOR A DIP OR WITH CHICKEN AND PASTA.

- LOTS OF CHERRY OR VINE TOMATOES
- 4 GARLIC CLOVES
- 1 SMALL RED ONION, ROUGHLY CHOPPED
- 1 HANDFUL OF FRESH BASIL
- SALT AND BLACK PEPPER
- GLUG OF OIL

Squash & Chilli Muffins

PREP

Method

1. Grab a mixing bowl and throw in all of the ingredients apart from the seeds, bit of the chilli and a bit of the Parmesan.
2. Take out a wooden spoon and mix like you've never mixed before.
3. Place twelve muffin cases into the muffin tray and lightly oil. Spoon in mixture, evenly. Sprinkle over the remainder of the seeds, chilli and cheese.
4. Place on the bottom shelf of a preheated oven at 180°C and cook for approx 35–40 minutes until golden brown on top.
5. These are an amazing savoury snack!

- ½ butternut squash, grated
- 2 spring onions, chopped
- 3 fresh red chillies, chopped
- 6 eggs
- 3 tbsp cottage cheese
- 250g gluten-free self-raising flour
- Good handful of Parmesan cheese, grated
- Good pinch of two different type of seeds
  – poppy, pumpkin, sunflower or sesame

Steve Gilbert

Serious Mental Illness
Living Experience Consultant

WHAT IS YOUR EXPERIENCE WITH MENTAL ILLNESS?

In 2008, I had a serious depressive episode. Prior to this, my life had been going very well. In 2005, I graduated from university. I was teaching and was very happy with my work.

I had a girlfriend and we were looking for a house. I was twenty-four. I then decided not to be a teacher and knew I wanted to become a photographer. However, the step from wanting to become one and setting up a business was a huge step. I broke up with my girlfriend and felt I was descending into a spiral, in which I didn't know what to do or how to get out of it. Every door seemed to close. I became more isolated and isolated myself. I started to step away from people and remove myself from everyone. I went to the GP and said that I felt I was starting to get depressed, and that I was having suicidal thoughts, which felt strong. I asked the doctor whether I could get some talking therapy. The doctor's answer was "You don't have cancer, so there's no talking therapy for you." The doctor wrote a prescription for antidepressants, but I refused to take them on their own.

I felt that if I found a career to follow I would feel better. I didn't sleep, I worked all the time and I felt increasingly stressed. I saw different doctors. I felt suicidal most of the time and could not see any other way than taking my own life. I went with a good friend, Kathy, to one doctor and expressed that I was seriously suicidal. The doctor's response was that if someone felt this suicidal, they would take their life anyway. Kathy and I left the surgery baffled.

Things took an even worse turn in 2012. All I could think about at this stage was dying and I googled ways of taking my life. I found websites that talked about suicide and how to do it. I planned to take an overdose, as I had been sitting with a razor blade for days and realised I couldn't do it that way. I felt an overdose was the best way for me. On the internet, it mentioned that you should tell someone if you were planning to take your own life, so I told Kathy. She explained to me how long it would take to actually die from an overdose. Kathy then called the Samaritans and support came into place for me, even though their diagnosis of depression wasn't a surprise. Sadly, my Grandad died a few weeks later.

I tried different career avenues and was still having deep depressive stages. I still planned to take my own life and felt that I had failed everyone. I started researching how I could make my suicide look like an accident. I researched car accidents and how it could be done on a wet day, so it would seem like an accident. I threw myself down the stairs to injure myself, but survived.

My suicidal thoughts continued and I had a manic episode. I was sectioned. I spent ten days at the Queen Elizabeth Hospital Birmingham. Because the habit of my normal life was taken away, it helped me. I was then transferred to a place just north of Erdington. I was there for eleven days and it was awful. I was finally diagnosed with bipolar disorder and I accepted the diagnosis quickly. I tried various medications, but some of it made me feel like a zombie and as though I was debilitating.

What really helped me was to have the same doctor and nurses, as it helped me to build relationships and to have some continuity. I was not against medication at all, so long as it is coupled with talking therapy and done in the right way.

Between 2010 and 2015, I managed to level myself out with talking therapy and medication. However, even though I felt that things were at a level at this stage, I experienced difficulties with my family. I realised that some of my depression stemmed from family issues. In the summer of 2015, I had another suicidal period and realised that a lot of my psychological imbalance stemmed from childhood. I had another diagnosis of complex PTSD (Post Traumatic Stress Disorder). I have since had a lot of talking therapy in order to understand that this was long-term psychological abuse. I feel that I am now having an active recovery and I am able to function as part of society. I take my medication; I sees a psychiatrist; and I have people to check in on me and how I am. I am actively trying to balance my life.

Helping other people within mental health helps me. I started to volunteer with Time to Change and this helps me in my day-to-day life. I am almost hooked on volunteering! Doing the work with Time to Change makes sense of my life. I feel that there is nothing I can own or have to make my life better. I have been depressed in various affluent and less affluent areas, and I strongly believe that money does not make you happy, nor does it stop depression or mental health challenges.

WHAT DO YOU DO TO KEEP YOURSELF ON A STEADY LEVEL?

I love photography. I have also started looking at my lifestyle and how to eat healthier. I try to get more exercise into my life. A routine is key for me, as I need routine to keep myself balanced. I love my job and I have learnt how to time-manage my diary effectively, knowing, for example, to give myself time either side of large projects as I need time to recover. I also recognise that sleep is very important.

WHAT IS YOUR FAVOURITE FOOD?

Chicken fajitas is my favourite, because it is easy and tasty and great for sharing.

"I'm better at keeping myself well, than the people who are well all the time"

— Steve Gilbert

Roasted Spicy Chickpeas

- 2 cans of chickpeas, drained
- Glug of olive oil
- 1 tsp ground cumin
- 1 tsp chilli powder
- ½ tsp cayenne pepper
- ½ tsp sea salt

Method

1. Preheat oven to 200ºC.
2. Bung all of the ingredients into a bowl and mix. Tip the mixture onto a baking tray and roast for 30–40 minutes.
3. Try different spice mixes. **PREP**

SALT & PEPPER VEGGIE CRISPS

- SWEET POTATO, CARROT, PARSNIP, BEETROOT
- GLUG OF OIL
- SALT AND PEPPER

PREP

METHOD

1. PREHEAT OVEN TO 200ºC.
2. SLICE THE VEGETABLES VERY THIN, IDEALLY WITH A MANDOLIN, BUT IF NOT WITH A SHARP KNIFE.
3. BUNG ALL INGREDIENTS INTO A BOWL AND MIX. LINE UP THE VEGETABLES NICE AND FLAT AND NOT OVERLAPPING.
4. THROW IN THE OVEN FOR 10 MINUTES, THEN TAKE OUT AND TURN ALL OF THE CRISPS OVER. STICK BACK IN THE OVEN FOR ANOTHER 8 OR SO MINUTES, KEEPING AN EYE ON THEM. ONCE OUT, LEAVE THEM ON A TRAY TO CRISP UP. DONE!

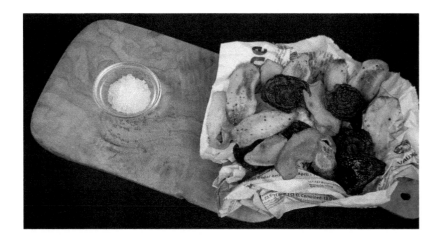

SALMON, PEA & PARMESAN FRITTATA

- Handful of baby new potatoes, sliced
- Handful of frozen peas
- 6 large eggs
- Big dollop of crème fraîche
- Handful of parmesan, finely grated
- Small handful of Chives, finely chopped
- 4 Slices of smoked salmon, cut into strips

Method

1. Preheat the oven to 180°C. Cook the potatoes until just tender and bung in the peas at the last minute. Line a twelve-hole muffin tin with squares of baking paper.

2. In a jug, whisk together the eggs, crème fraîche and Parmesan. Stick the sliced potatoes and peas into the muffin holes, then top with the smoked salmon and pour over the egg mixture. Bake for 20–25 minutes until golden on top.

PREP

RAOK

Give a £10 gift card for a restaurant to someone entering that restaurant

Watch a neighbour's children while they run errands

Offer to take a photo of people trying to take one of themselves

Put envelopes with money and a nice note inside on random car windshields

Take in your neighbour's bins

Read a book to someone

Pay the toll for a few cars behind you

Forgive someone

Send pizza anonymously to a family you know could use a night off from making dinner

NOTES

_____
_____
_____
_____
_____
_____
_____
_____
_____
_____
_____
_____
_____
_____
_____
_____
_____
_____
_____
_____
_____
_____

NOTES

SHEPHERD PIE SKINS

RUN

- 250g mince
- Glug of olive oil
- 1 onion
- 1 garlic clove, minced
- 1 carrot, diced
- 1 small tin of sweetcorn
- Handful of frozen peas
- 2 tbsp flour
- ½ pint of stock
- ½ cup of water
- Twist of salt and pepper
- ½ tsp dried thyme
- ½ tsp dried oregano
- 4 large potatoes
- Splash of milk to mash

1. Preheat oven to 180ºC. Prick the spuds and throw in the microwave on high for 5 minutes. Wait for the ping and then turn and throw in again. Take out and slice the tops off, scoop out the insides and place in a bowl. Mash spud with a splash of milk.
2. Meanwhile, heat up a glug of oil in a pan, throw in the garlic and onion and cook until soft. Now, bung in mince until brown and cooked, sprinkle over flour and stir. Bung in everything else and bring to a simmer for the sauce to reduce.
3. Add the onion and garlic and sauté for 2 minutes until softened.
4. Spoon the mince into each of the potato skins and top with the mashed potato. Fluff up with a fork.
5. Bang in the oven for 15–20 minutes until brown and crispy.

- 4 chicken legs, thighs or breast
- 1 bell pepper, 1 sweet potato and 1 red onion, all roughly chopped
- Handful of cherry tomatoes, mushrooms and broccoli florets
- 4 tbsp balsamic vinegar
- 3 tbsp extra virgin olive oil
- 2 cloves of garlic
- 1 tsp herb de province

Method

1. Grab a bowl and bung in the balsamic vinegar, oil, garlic and herbs. Then, throw in the chicken and sweet potato, and mix. Take out a bowl and spread the mix on a baking tray covered in greaseproof paper. Stick on the top shelf of a preheated oven at 200°C.

2. While they are roasting, roughly chop up the remainder of the vegetables and put in the same bowl with the marinade. After about twenty minutes, take out the chicken and spuds and pour on the vegetables. Evenly spread out.

3. Throw back on the top shelf for an extra 20 minutes until the vegetables and chicken are cooked.

4. Chop up and throw over some fresh parsley. Tuck in and enjoy!

One-pan Roasted Chicken & Vegetables

STANDARD PUSH-UP

There's a reason why this one is a classic.

With your hands a shoulder-width apart, keep your feet flexed at hip distance and tighten your core.

UPPER BODY

Bend your elbows until your chest reaches the ground and then push back up (make sure to keep your elbow tucked close to your body).
That's one!

DIAMOND PUSH-UP

UPPER BODY

Jay-Z would approve!

These push-ups get pimped out with a diamond-shaped hand position (situate them so that your thumbs and index fingers touch). This hand readjustment will give those triceps some extra love.

"IF IT DOESN'T CHALLENGE YOU, IT DOESN'T CHANGE YOU"

Reverse Fly
UPPER BODY

For DIY dumbbells, grab two cans or two bottles of water. Stand up straight with one foot in front of the other and your front knee slightly bent.

With your palms facing each other and your abs engaged, bend forward slightly from your waist and extend arms out to the side, squeezing your shoulder blades. Repeat.

"Your body is worth FIGHTing for"

"Risk is the down payment of SUCCESS"

Triceps Dip

et seated near a step or
ench. Sit on the floor
ith your knees slightly
ent, then grab the edge
f the elevated surface
nd straighten your arms.

end them to a 90-degree
ngle and straighten
gain while your heels
ush towards the floor.
or some extra fire, reach
our right arm out while
fting your left leg.

"When you think about quitting,
think about why you STARTed"

"Don't limit your challenges.
CHALLENGE your limits"

Jason Nelson

Former Police Officer

WHAT IS YOUR EXPERIENCE WITH MENTAL ILLNESS?

In 2008, after battling depression for around six months, I attempted suicide several times over a period of weeks. I knew something was wrong, but hadn't yet been diagnosed. It was only after attempting suicide that I was officially diagnosed with depression and anxiety.

I moved to Australia from the UK in 2006 as an experienced police officer for a new life down under and a new career with Western Australia Police, as part of an international police recruiting programme. In late 2007, I was moved to help set up a high-risk covert team, based upon my previous experience and expertise in the field in the UK.

After about two months in the team, the detective senior sergeant made it clear that he didn't like that I had been 'parachuted' into the team and, along with the detective sergeant, began to set me up to fail in operational situations and tried to claim I didn't have the skill set to be on the team. Unfortunately, I was a victim of my own success. Each time the team sent me off on a job, I came back with results, which appeared to motivate the bullying even more.

I just wanted to get on with the job. We had only been in Australia for a short period of time. My wife and children had settled in well to their new life, but I was struggling. Due to the bullying at work and what felt like insurmountable pressures, my mental fitness spiralled out of control and I reached a point where I couldn't take the pain anymore. I felt like a burden and that I wasn't strong enough to look after my family. Something had to give, so I thought it would be easier for me to take my own life and remove the pain in this way.

Thankfully, I didn't. I ended up breaking down and telling my wife. I broke my cover at work and gave up my job. Sadly, WA Police didn't provide much support other than referring me to a psychiatrist. The psychiatrist was a Vietnam veteran and we got on very well, and the talking certainly helped.

My recovery went well until about four years ago when I had a routine hernia operation. I woke up from the operation feeling tired. My family saw me for a while and then left me to get some rest. I wasn't sure how long I slept for, but I woke up to a heartbeat of 160bpm and climbing. My heart rate continued to rise and rise. I called the nurses, who came to help. One of the nurses asked, "Have you seen his neck?" I felt as though my heart was in my throat. Within seconds, there were around fifteen people in the room, a full crash team had been called and my heart rate kept climbing. I clearly remember saying to the nurse that I didn't want to die today, that I was not ready to die.

The medical team pumped me full of meds and after four hours, my heart rate slowed. They did tests on my heart and couldn't find anything wrong with it. I have since learnt that it was more than likely a sleep-induced panic attack. I have never had one before nor since.

After this, I began to get PTSD symptoms, including flashbacks, from my hospital incident and from my childhood.

My anxiety levels were through the roof. I couldn't sleep; I felt irritable; I lived with night terrors and had flashbacks during the day. It sent me down another spiral. I remember breaking down one day on my daily commute on the train, sobbing my heart out. Not one person asked if I was okay. Here was a grown man sobbing his heart out and not one person checked on me. I got off the train, walked across the platform, got a train back and went straight to my doctor. I was diagnosed with PTSD, which I have been treated for since.

To compound things, My youngest daughter attempted suicide in 2015, twice in the space of three months. Our family have spent the last two years helping her. The anxiety I feels as a parent is huge, as my wife and I struggle to leave our daughter alone and lock things away that she could potentially harm herself with. Thankfully, she has come through it. She is at college now, studying to become a nurse, and has grown into a wonderful young woman. What I went through, both with my daughter and personally, has made me want to change people's perceptions about mental health. I feels it's time to talk openly about it.

WHAT DO YOU DO TO KEEP YOURSELF ON A STEADY LEVEL?

I am a keen distance runner and I have completed twenty-two marathons to date. I credit distance running as one of my most powerful therapies. It helps me be mindful about my breathing and I meditates while running. I sees a psychologist regularly, still on medication and I listen to mindfulness apps. I also follow weekly teachings by a British monk, Ajahn Brahm, at Buddhist Society of Western Australia, who teaches in a lighthearted and comical way. I find the Buddhist way interesting and calming.

I am also a volunteer peer support worker for the Sirens of Silence charity and Western Australian Police Force. I have found that giving back helps him, too.

WHAT'S YOUR FAVOURITE FOOD?

I love Thai food, as well as coconut-infused and spicy food. I also loves Ramen.

Beef and Broccoli Stir Fry

RUN

- 3 tbsp cornstarch
- 120 ml water
- ½ tsp garlic powder
- 1lb steak
- Glug of oil
- Handful of Broccoli florets
- 1 small onion, cut into wedges
- 60ml soy sauce
- 1 tsp ground ginger

Method

1. In a bowl, bung in 2 tbsp of cornstarch, 2 tbsp water and garlic powder, and mix until smooth. Add the beef and give it a toss.
2. In a large pan or wok, over a medium-high heat, throw in the beef with a glug of oil. Cook to the desired taste and remove.
3. Stir-fry the broccoli and onion in the remaining oil for 4–5 minutes, then throw the beef back in.
4. Mix together the soy sauce, ginger and remaining cornstarch and water. Mix until smooth and pour in the pan.

Chicken & Chorizo Stew

RUN

Method

1. Bung the spices and herbs together in a bowl and mix.
2. Grab hold of your large casserole dish and throw on the hob with a glug of oil and the chorizo. Next, throw in the chicken skin side down, until brown and then remove from dish.
3. Deglaze the pan with water and then glug in the oil with onions, garlic and half the spice mix. Now, time to throw in the chickpeas and tomatoes fill the can back up with water and throw that in with the stock cube.
4. Bring to a simmer and throw in the chicken and chorizo. Simmer for thirty minutes. Take lid off and bung in the rest of the ingredients. Simmer for another 10 or so minutes until chicken is fully cooked and the sauce has reduced.
5. Return the chicken and chorizo to the pan, then cover and simmer for about 30 minutes. Stir in the olives, spice and chilli flakes. Cook, uncovered, for another 10 minutes or until the chicken is fully cooked and reduced

- Glug of olive oil
- 1 whole Chorizo, peeled and cubed
- 8 chicken thighs (skin on, bone in)
- 1 large onion, chopped
- 2 garlic cloves, crushed
- Glug of water to deglaze the pan
- 1 tsp thyme, oregano and paprika
- ½ tsp ground cumin and chilli
- 1 can of chickpeas
- 1 can of chopped tomatoes
- 1 vegetable or chicken stock cube, crumbled
- Handful of green pitted olives
- Salt and freshly ground pepper
- ¼ tsp dried chilli flakes

Want some SUPERPOWERS? Lie face down with your arms and legs extended. Keeping your torso as still as possible, simultaneously raise your arms and legs to form a small curve in your body.

CAPE IS OPTIONAL

SUPERMAN

UPPER BODY

Richard Taylor

Mental health campaigner
and writer'

WHAT'S YOUR EXPERIENCE WITH MENTAL ILLNESS?

Mental illness usually starts with a diagnosis, but for so many people the diagnosis is, in fact, the mid or end point after a long struggle. I didn't know what was wrong with me until I was fifteen years old, but I had suffered since I was five or six years old. I started displaying symptoms of OCD without knowing what it was. My first memory of OCD was ripping labels off CDs and books. If it had a label, I would have to rip it off. If the label wouldn't come off perfectly, it was a huge problem. Other people would have called my reaction a temper tantrum or a strop, but for me it was a serious thing. I didn't want the item if the label hadn't been ripped off properly. If a book had a rip or a bend or had been damaged in any way, I couldn't keep it as it didn't feel right to me.

When my parents split up, I really struggled. I had massive abandonment issues and feared that my dad would leave me as well. I don't blame my mum and I understand why my parents split up. This led to me seeing a psychiatrist – or, at least, that is what I thought. However, since talking to my dad, I realised that the session was for my dad and that it was my dad who talked for an hour while I played with toys in another room. I clearly remember telling my dad I didn't want to go to the sessions anymore. I got increasingly angry with everything. I would punch my dad and kick him because I didn't want to go to school and leave my dad. I would pretend to be ill and hit my head against stuff to hurt myself, so that I wouldn't have to go to school. Teachers would have to sit and hold me down, as I wouldn't stay. I would also try and make my dad stay with me. This carried on until the end of primary school.

Things settled down for a while, until I was fifteen years old. One day, I was scared to touch the carpet in my bedroom. It got to the point that I felt scared to leave my bed as it meant I had to touch or step onto the carpet. I asked my dad for a new chair so I could play my video games, but instead I used the chair to put at the end of the bed so I could get out of my room without touching the carpet. This fear got increasingly worse and soon I was not able to touch the carpet on the landing, the walls in school and door handles. I stopped being able to do my schoolwork. For a kid who was always punctual and always did my work, the teachers quickly picked up on the change in me. It was the first time my dad discovered what was happening and he took me to the doctors. There, I explained my fears and the doctor very quickly said that he thought that I had OCD and clinical depression.

Within two months, I was given one-to-one counselling. It really helped. I went from not going anywhere to going and buying hand gel, so I could quickly use the hand gel if I touched something while out. However, I then used the hand gel all the time and this turned into an obsession. My hands cracked through using the gel so often. When I was seventeen, I got severe chicken pox and had to go into hospital, where I was wrapped in dressings. For someone like me, who showers every day, to lie in a bed for a week, not shower and lie in my own wounds was horrendous. It sparked another period of doubt, fear, worry and depression, and I stopped going out. I stopped going to sixth form and lost my place as head boy. I couldn't drive my car, and everything that made me feel free and full of purpose was taken away from me. I eventually became housebound. I was incredibly fearful of people in the street coughing and sneezing near me, as well as the pollution from cars. I stopped going out for about three months. With help and support, I managed to go outside in the garden and go out a little. Soon afterwards, however, I became bedbound for nine months. At the time, I was staying with the family of an ex-girlfriend. In addition, my grandad was dying of leukemia and my grandmother was looking after him. My dad was working full time, looking after my grandparents and coming to see me.

A typical day for me would be that my ex-girlfriend would set up the television for the day, as I couldn't touch the remote, and then she'd go to work. All of the family would be working or at school for the day. My dad would come and see me at 11am and help me with basic hygiene. However, if the flannel touched the sink, I would want a new flannel. I couldn't use the shower, as I couldn't stand in it. Each day, my dad would have to provide clean towels, flannels and a new toothbrush. My dad would get two or three new toothbrushes ready in case there was a problem with one of them. I would also have to have new clothes, new plastic plates, new plastic cutlery and new bedding every day. I was nineteen years old and had lost all of his dignity. I had lost myself. I lost weight. I went from 12 stone to 8 stone. I was a prisoner of OCD for nine months.

If I saw something on the television or something happened that reminded me of my childhood, I would have to stay in for twenty-four hours. If a fly touched me, I would have to stay in for another day. My life was controlled by how many days I had to stay in and be bedbound. One day, my dad completely broke down in tears and said that he couldn't watch his son die any more. He said either we both ended it together, or that he would call the hospital and section me. My dad knew that I would kill myself if I ended up in a mental health hospital. My dad felt powerless. For the first time, I properly saw what my condition was doing to my dad. Through the power of my mind and for the love I had for my dad, those nine months of imprisonment disappeared. We made a plan to help me so that the environment wouldn't, quite literally, kill me. I would move to live with my mum and uncle in Blackpool. I said goodbye to his dad, thinking I would never see him again. I felt I could never come back to this place again. After this, I gradually tried to build up a new life. The first year was great, but it become evident that I had run away from the problem rather than dealing with the problem. I went to college and started going out and drinking.

I remembered a conversation I had with my dad before moving to Blackpool. My dad had mentioned a name and the name had hit me like a tonne of bricks. The name took me right back to my childhood and I knew that that was why I am the way I am. It took me back to a memory. I told my dad everything about my fears, feelings and the memories from my childhood. My dad told me I would be fine. We could do this together and get help.

In Blackpool, I began to stop running away from the memory of my childhood and accepted that it needed addressing and should be dealt with rather than run away from. I had to perform a mental autopsy on myself. My life changed even more dramatically when I picked up a book in a bookshop written by Pamela Stephenson Connolly "Sex Life: How Our Sexual Encounters and Experiences Define Who We Are". The book was about how sex is present throughout our lives, from the womb to death. I read the book and felt that I was not the only one who had experienced things that I thought had made me a bad person. From the age of seven to thirteen, I had experienced sexual encounters with friends of both sexes. At the time, I had no concept of what it all meant or was. At fifteen, I had believed that all of these encounters were very bad. Then, when I read Connolly's book, I realised that what I had experienced wasn't a bad thing. I had punished myself for years for something that was simply childhood experimentation and exploration. I had always thought it was wrong, horrible and sordid.

Once I accepted this, I felt a great sense of release and felt able to say the names of those I had been experimental with. I could go back to my life with my dad. I hadn't seen him for eighteen months. From then on, my recovery involved feeling acceptance and empathy for myself, and talking about my journey. I started to treat myself better. Although I still get bad episodes with depression and OCD, I now have the tools to help me out. I know my brain lies to me and that I don't have to listen to my OCD. The irony is that OCD saved me from killing myself as the OCD wouldn't let me leave my bed to do so!

WHAT DO YOU DO TO KEEP YOURSELF ON A STEADY LEVEL?

I check in with myself. I stop and make sure I understand my thoughts. I have learnt to stop my trail of thoughts when they begin to spiral. I talk about my experiences and I am an advocate for the Time to Change campaign. I try to do all the small things that make me smile. I love my video games and doing things that make me happy. I read and listen to music and talk to people.

WHAT'S YOUR FAVOURITE FOOD?

Pizza!

1. MARINATE CHICKEN WITH LEMONS, OREGANO, GARLIC AND A TWIST OF SALT. LEAVE IN FRIDGE FOR AT LEAST 20 MINUTES, BUT BETTER OVERNIGHT.

2. PREHEAT OVEN TO 180ºC. HEAT UP PAN WITH A GLUG OF OIL AND BUNG IN THE CHICKEN SKIN, SIDE DOWN, UNTIL BROWN AND THEN TURN OVER. TAKE OUT AND PUT ON A BOARD. SAVE THE MARINADE.

3. CLEAN OIL OUT OF THE PAN AND THEN PUT BACK ON THE HOB. BUNG IN ONIONS UNTIL SOFT AND THROW IN ALL OF THE OTHER BITS AND BOBS, INCLUDING THE MARINADE.

4. LET THE LIQUID COME TO A SIMMER AND LET IT DO SO FOR A FURTHER 30 SECONDS. PLACE THE CHICKEN ON TOP, THEN PUT A LID ON IT. BAKE IN THE OVEN FOR 35 MINUTES.

5. REMOVE THE LID AND THEN THROW IT BACK IN THE OVEN FOR ANOTHER 10 MINUTES OR UNTIL THE RICE IS TENDER AND THE LIQUID HAS GONE.

GREEK CHICKEN
RUN

- 5 CHICKEN THIGHS, SKIN ON, BONE IN
- 1–2 LEMONS, USE THE ZEST AND 4 TBSP LEMON JUICE
- 1 TBSP DRIED OREGANO
- 4 GARLIC CLOVES, MINCED
- GOOD TWIST OF SALT
- GLUG OF OIL
- 1 SMALL ONION, CHOPPED
- 1 CUP OF LONG GRAIN RICE
- ½ PINT STOCK
- ¼ PINT WATER
- 1 TBSP DRIED OREGANO
- GOOD TWIST OF SALT AND PEPPER

CHICKEN CURRY

RUN

4 chicken breasts, chopped
1 large onion, chopped
1 small tin of tomato puree
Glug of oil

Cinnamon stick
Jug of water
4 cardamom pods
2 bay leaves
1 star anise
1tsp of garlic paste,

ginger paste, salt, cumin, garam masala, curry powder, chilli powder and turmeric
Handful of coriander

Method

1. In a large pan, glug in the oil and heat. Throw in the onions with cinnamon, cardamom, bay leaves, star anise, garlic paste and ginger paste, and cook until the onions are soft. Then, it's time to throw in the chicken and tomato puree.

2. Give it a good mix, turn down the heat and place on the lid. Cook for 20 minutes or until the water from the chicken has reduced, stirring occasionally. Bung in the remaining spices, mix and cook for a further minute. The smell now should be unreal.

3. Pour in a little bit of water and stir, then pour in enough water to cover the chicken and bring to a boil. Continue to cook until the sauce has reduced and thickened up.

4. There! You have a beauty of a curry that is so easy to cook. Serve with a sprinkle of coriander.

DIRTY RICE

1 bowl of cooked rice
1 packet of pork mince
A few slices of bacon, chopped
1 bell pepper, sliced
1 red onion, diced
A pint chicken stock

1 tbsp Cajun
Good glug of Worcestershire sauce
2 sticks of celery, chopped
3 spring onions, chopped

Method
1. Glug in oil and bung in the onions, pork mince and bacon until they are nicely browned.
2. Throw in the Cajun and Worcestershire sauce. Stir and allow to cook for another minute. Then, throw in the celery and stock.
3. Stir in the peppers and spring onion. Cook for a minute or two, until they just start to soften.
4. Finally, bung in the cooked rice, giving it a good flip, and mix to bring it all together.

RUN

MOROCCAN CHICKEN DIPPERS WITH HERBY YOGURT DIP

RUN

Method

1. Preheat oven to 180°C.
2. You need three bowls – this is a great tasting dish, but rubbish for washing-up duties! Put the flour, salt and pepper in one bowl, the eggs in another and the breadcrumbs and Ras el hanout in the third.
3. Bung some of the chicken into the flour and toss, then transfer to the eggs for a dunk and then flip into the breadcrumbs. Once fully coated, place onto a baking tray lined with greaseproof paper.
4. Bang in the oven and bake for approximately 20 minutes or until the chicken is cooked.
5. For the dip, throw everything in a bowl and mix. Easy!

Chicken

- 4 chicken fillets, sliced into dipper-sized bits
- 2 large eggs
- ½ a bowl of plain flour
- ½ a bowl of breadcrumbs
- 2 tbsp Ras el hanout
- 2 tbsp vegetable oil

Dip

- 200 g plain Greek yogurt
- Salt and pepper
- Squeeze of Lemon juice
- 2 tbsp chives, chopped
- 2 tbsp parsley, chopped
- 2 tbsp coriander, chopped

Stuart Wildsmith

Lecturer

WHAT IS YOUR EXPERIENCE WITH MENTAL ILLNESS?

My story goes back to my childhood. My mum and dad split up when I was three weeks old, and my mum moved to Birmingham. I never knew my dad, as my mum kept his identity from me. I didn't know why she did at the time, but it turned out my dad was an alcoholic. I didn't know anything about this until his mum unfortunately passed away when I was nineteen.

I had a rough time at school and didn't enjoy it. In the early 1990s, mental health didn't have as high a profile as today and it was often brushed under the carpet. When I left home, I became a little isolated and bored and began to drink a lot. I went into a downward spiral. I had a successful job, working in London in pubs and restaurants. I didn't particularly feel bad about myself, but still drank a lot. I feels this was down to the environment I was working in.

I had it good in my twenties. However, when I was thirty, I moved back to Birmingham and things started to go downhill. I began to drink more and isolated myself by not hanging around with my mates as much. Things got gradually worse and I was sectioned in 2004. I went to the doctor and explained that I didn't feel well. The first thing the doctor asked was "How much do you drink?" I replied with "Quite a lot." I realised I was using alcohol as an emotional crutch. Everyone told me to stop drinking, but I couldn't see the wood for the trees. Everyone was telling me what to do and I couldn't do it. It got so bad that I would sometimes wake up at 4am and have a drink. I was sectioned and taken to the Queen Elizabeth Psychiatric Hospital for three weeks, because I had threatened to take my own life.

A lot of my depression was down to alcohol and I later found out that my dad had died of alcoholism in 2009. I came out of hospital thinking I was a changed man, but I wasn't as the drinking continued, though I was nowhere near as bad as it had been. I linked my depression and drinking to work, as well as the fact that a lot of my friends had gone to grammar school and I hadn't. With my mum dying, I had never gone onto further education. I felt self-loathing for not fulfilling what I had thought was part of my life plan.

In 2011, things came to a head, when I had another episode with drinking. I got an opportunity to go and work at a college I had studied at, which is now a university. I took the opportunity with both hands and didn't want to screw it up, as I was now thirty-eight. I stopped drinking – stopping completely was, and still is, the best thing for me. It is only now that I am realising how many of my peers, from college and school, are in the same boat as I used to be. There is something about our generation and alcohol that hasn't mixed! Something went wrong. Alcohol and pub culture are social things, and there is a pressure to drink.

I can now clearly see how many people have a problem with alcohol. People have asked me for help. I don't feel I am a great person who can shout from the rooftops about how I quit and what worked for me may not work for anyone else. What I changed were the simple things. I had a bath every day, started eating properly, stopped drinking and started exercising. When I was at my lowest, I couldn't be bothered to have a bath every day. I had to find his own self-worth again. I kept in mind that it doesn't matter where you've been, it's where you are going that matters.

I never took any professional advice when I decided to stop drinking, after the doctor told me it was paramount to do so. I decided to take antidepressants and I am still on them now, six years on. It is a low dose and I am quite happy about taking them. When I stopped drinking, I had to rediscover who I was, which was a massive learning curve. The first year off alcohol was very strange and it was brilliant waking up every morning feeling okay. I felt free after giving up alcohol. I had been very close to losing my house and my wife, and I could've been left with nothing at all. I therefore feels lucky in the way that things have panned out. And everything that has happened since I gave up drinking has been down to me, which is the best feeling ever.

My advice to anyone in this position is to never give up. You never know what is around the corner. I now have a fantastic job at a university, earn good money, I am studying for a Master's degree, have three lovely children and a fantastic wife, lives in a great house and have a great car. And all of this is down to the fact that I stopped drinking.

WHAT DO YOU DO TO KEEP YOURSELF ON A STEADY LEVEL?

I keep myself balanced by looking after myself. I do things that make me happy.

I drink plenty of water and love to cook. I have an active life and takes part in my kids' activities. I also eat lots of fruit. I try to put a positive spin on everything and I am thankful for what I have now.

WHAT IS YOUR FAVOURITE FOOD?

Ice cream! The power of ice cream should never, ever be underestimated! Ice cream sorts everything out.

Lime & Chilli Turkey

- 4 TURKEY BREASTS
- JUICE AND ZEST OF 1 LIME
- GLUG OF OLIVE OIL
- HANDFUL OF CORIANDER, CHOPPED
- 2 GARLIC CLOVES, CHOPPED
- TWIST OF SALT
- 1 TSP HONEY
- 1 TSP RED CHILLI FLAKES
- ½ TSP GROUND CUMIN

METHOD

1. MIX MARINADE IN A BOWL AND THROW IN THE TURKEY. COVER AND STICK IN THE FRIDGE FOR AT LEAST AN HOUR, BUT BETTER OVERNIGHT.
2. HEAT UP A GRIDDLE ON THE HOB OR THE BARBEQUE AND GRILL FOR 5 MINUTES ON EACH SIDE UNTIL COOKED. THIS RECIPE IS GREAT IN PITTA BREAD WITH A SALAD.

- 4 PORK CHOPS
- 1 TBSP OLIVE OIL, SESAME OIL, GINGER PASTE
- 60ML SOY SAUCE
- 2 TBSP HONEY AND SRIRACHA SAUCE
- 4 GARLIC CLOVES, MINCED
- GOOD TWIST OF SALT AND BLACK PEPPER

METHOD
1. PREHEAT OVEN TO 200ºC.
2. GRAB A BOWL, BUNG IN ALL OF THE INGREDIENTS AND MARINADE PORK FOR A GOOD HOUR.
3. HEAT UP PAN ON A MEDIUM HEAT, THROW IN THE PORK CHOPS AND COOK ON BOTH SIDES FOR ABOUT 5 MINUTES EACH UNTIL BROWN.
4. POUR OVER THE REST OF THE MARINADE AND BAKE IN THE OVEN FOR 10 MINUTES.

RUN KOREAN PORK

Method

1. Preheat oven to 200°C. Line a large baking sheet with greaseproof paper.
2. In a small bowl, combine the egg and the milk and whisk together.
3. In a large sandwich bag, combine the flour, breadcrumbs, salt, pepper, powder, garlic, coriander and chilli flakes. Close the bag and shake until mixed.
4. Here is the messy and fun bit! Drop the chicken into the bag and shake a few times. Then, give it a dip into the wet stuff and back into the bag. Once coated, stick onto the baking tray, spaced out.
5. Cook for 20-25 minutes until nice and crispy. Then, stick on a platter next to sweet potato fries and dips. Put on a movie and enjoy!

- 4 chicken breasts
- 1 bowl of flour
- 1 bowl of breadcrumbs
- Twist of salt and pepper
- 1tsp chilli flakes and garlic powder
- Fresh coriander, chopped
- 1 bowl of milk
- 1 egg

RUN

Popcorn Chilli Chicken

Method

1. Grab a saucepan, bung in the oil and garlic and turn the heat up high.
2. Chuck in chicken and fry it until it is browned. Then, bung in the vegetables and stir well over a high heat.
3. Throw in the risotto rice and stir it in with the meat, just for a few seconds, so it's well mixed. Add the white wine, keep the heat high and keep stirring. Once the wine has cooked into the rice, start adding ladles of the stock.
4. Turn the heat down so it only simmers. The key to a good risotto is to stir often, to add the stock slowly and to let it simmer. Once the first ladle of stock has soaked into the rice, keep adding ladles of stock and stir often. Once all of the stock has gone, test your risotto and make sure the rice is cooked.
5. Turn the heat off and stir in a good portion of grated Parmesan. Add a twist of salt and pepper. You can either stir in a bit of chopped parsley or sprinkle some

- Glug of oil
- 360g Risotto rice
- 1 litre of vegetable stock
- 2 garlic cloves, finely chopped
- ½ glass of white wine
- Half a Chorizo ring, chopped
- 2 chicken breasts, chopped
- Handful of cherry tomatoes, halved
- Handful of spinach
- Twist of salt and pepper
- Handful of Parmesan, grated
- Small handful of Parsley, chopped

Risotto Rice

RUN

Cooked by photographer

Method

1. Preheat oven to 200ºC. Grab a bowl and throw in the mozzarella, basil, vinegar, tomatoes and a good twist of salt and pepper. Mix.
2. Tear off a large piece of foil. Place the chopped courgette in the middle of the foil.
3. Put the turkey breast in between some baking paper and smack like a beauty to about ¼ inch thick. Place the mixture in the bowl into the middle of the turkey breast. Roll up the breast and use cocktail sticks to keep it in place. Pick it up and place on the courgette.
4. Carefully bring up the sides of the foil and make a bag, trying not to make a hole with the cocktail sticks. Bung on a baking tray and throw in the oven for 25 minutes. Serve with new potatoes and green vegetables.

RUN

- o Fresh mozzarella ball
- o Good handful of fresh basil
- o 10 cherry tomatoes, halved
- o 2 tsp balsamic vinegar
- o Good twist of salt and pepper
- o 2 courgettes
- o Glug of olive oil
- o ¼ tsp Italian seasoning
- o 2 turkey breasts

STUFFED TURKEY IN A BAG

- 4 CHICKEN BREASTS
- 2 TBSP THICK YOGURT
- 1 TBSP TAMARIND PASTE
- 1½ TSP RED CHILLI POWDER
- 1 TSP SALT
- 2 TSP GINGER PASTE
- 2 TSP GARLIC PASTE
- 2 TSP TOMATO PASTE OR PUREE
- 1 TBSP PAPRIKA POWDER

TASTE OF ZANZIBAR CHICKEN

METHOD

1. IT DOESN'T REALLY GET MUCH EASIER THAN THIS! CHOP THE CHICKEN INTO BITE-SIZED PIECES AND THROW IN A BOWL WITH EVERYTHING ELSE. LET IT MARINADE FOR AT LEAST TWO HOURS, BUT IDEALLY OVERNIGHT.
2. HEAT UP GRIDDLE OR BARBEQUE AND GRILL UNTIL THE CHICKEN IS COOKED, TURNING OCCASIONALLY. TO CHECK IT'S COOKED, RIP THE BIGGEST CHUNK OF CHICKEN OPEN AND MAKE SURE IT'S NOT PINK. THIS MEAL IS SO NICE THAT MY MOUTH IS WATERING WHILE TYPING!

- 1 POUND GROUND CHICKEN
- 1 LARGE RIPE AVOCADO, CUT INTO CHUNKS
- 1 GARLIC CLOVE, CHOPPED
- ⅓ CUP OF BREADCRUMBS
- 1 CHILLI, CHOPPED
- GOOD TWIST OF SALT AND PEPPER

TURKEY & AVOCADO BURGERS

METHOD

1. ADD ALL INGREDIENTS INTO A LARGE BOWL AND TOSS GENTLY.
2. SHAPE THE MIXTURE INTO PATTIES OF A DESIRED SIZE AND GRILL INSIDE OR OUT!

CHICKEN BOMBS

- 10 FILLETS OF CHICKEN
- 5 JALAPEÑOS
- BIG DOLLOP OF CREAM CHEESE, SOFTENED
- HANDFUL OF CHEDDAR
- CHEESE, GRATED
- SALT AND PEPPER TO TASTE
- 20 SLICES OF STREAKY BACON

RUN

METHOD

1. PUT THE CHICKEN FILLETS IN BETWEEN SOME BAKING PAPER AND SMACK UNTIL THEY ARE ABOUT 2.5CM THICK. TWIST SALT AND PEPPER ONTO THEM.
2. IN A BOWL, MIX THE TWO CHEESES. GRAB HOLD OF THE JALAPEÑOS AND CUT THEM IN HALF, TOP TO BOTTOM. REMOVE THE SEEDS AND FILL WITH CHEESE MIXTURE, THEN PLACE IN THE MIDDLE OF THE CHICKEN FILLET. WRAP THE CHICKEN AROUND THE JALAPEÑOS.
3. USING TWO SLICES OF BACON, WRAP THE CHICKEN UP AND TUCK IN THE ENDS TO SEAL IT IN A LOVELY PORK BLANKET.
4. THROW ON A HOT PLATE OR BARBEQUE FOR AROUND 20-25 MINUTES UNTIL THE CHICKEN JUICE RUNS CLEAR. BASTE WITH BARBEQUE SAUCE IF YOU FEEL LIKE PUSHING THE BOAT OUT.

- Big glug of olive oil
- Orange zest
- 200ml fresh orange juice
- A squeeze of fresh lime juice
- Big handful of coriander, finely chopped
- Handful of mint leaves, finely chopped
- 8 garlic cloves, minced
- 2 tsp oregano
- 2 tsp ground cumin
- Twist of salt and pepper
- Nice big lump of pork fillet

Method

1. In a food processor, bung in the orange juice, coriander, mint and smashed garlic cloves. Whiz until chopped. If you have no processor, chop like a beauty. Throw into a Ziploc bag, along with the rest of the oil, zest, lime juice, oregano and cumin.
2. Slice the pork to inch-thick medallions, add to the bag and mix. This needs to marinade for a good couple of hours, ideally overnight.
3. Fire up the barbeque or griddle pan and cook the medallions for roughly 20 minutes, turning every now and again.

RUN

Cuban
Marinated
Pork

- 1 red chilli, finely chopped
- Whole Iceberg lettuce
- 6 tsp dried oregano
- 6 tomatoes
- Good rip of Mint
- 2 lemons
- 1 cucumber, grated
- 1 pot of Greek yogurt
- 4 Pittas
- 3 garlic cloves, crushed
- 8 chicken thighs

Method
1. In a bowl, throw in the chopped chicken, half of the oregano, garlic, chilli and yogurt. Mix and stick in the fridge.
2. Tzatziki time! Pour the rest of the yogurt into another bowl. Bung in the chopped mint, a squeeze of lemon juice and the cucumber. Add a pinch of salt and pepper and mix.
3. Salsa time! Chop up the tomatoes. Add to a bowl with 3 tsp of oregano, salt, pepper and olive oil. Finely chop your lettuce.
4. Heat up a pan and bang in chicken to cook. While the chicken is cooking, warm up the pitta breads.
5. Build, build, build!

RUN

CHICKEN

GYROS

Potato Bowls

- 1 BAKED POTATO
- 1 EGG
- TWIST OF SALT AND PEPPER
- FRESH PARSLEY
- HAM
- SPRING ONION
- SPINACH

METHOD
- PREHEAT OVEN TO 200C
- TAKE TOP OF BAKED POTATO AND SCOOP OUT MAJORITY OF POTATO. LINE THE BOTTOM OF THE "BOWL" WITH SPINACH. CRACK IN THE EGG IN AND SPRINKLE THE ONION AND HAM ON TOP WITH PARSLEY.
- GOOD TWIST OF SALT AND PEPPER TO SEASON AND BUNG IN OVEN FOR ABOUT 25 MIN.

RUN

NOTES

NOTES

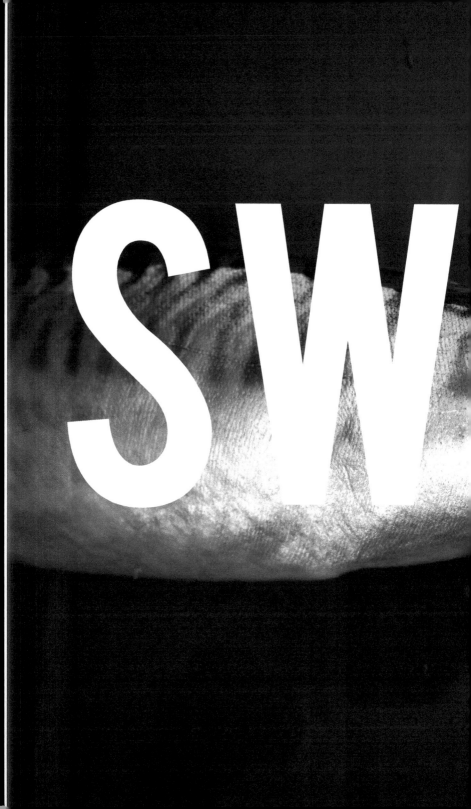

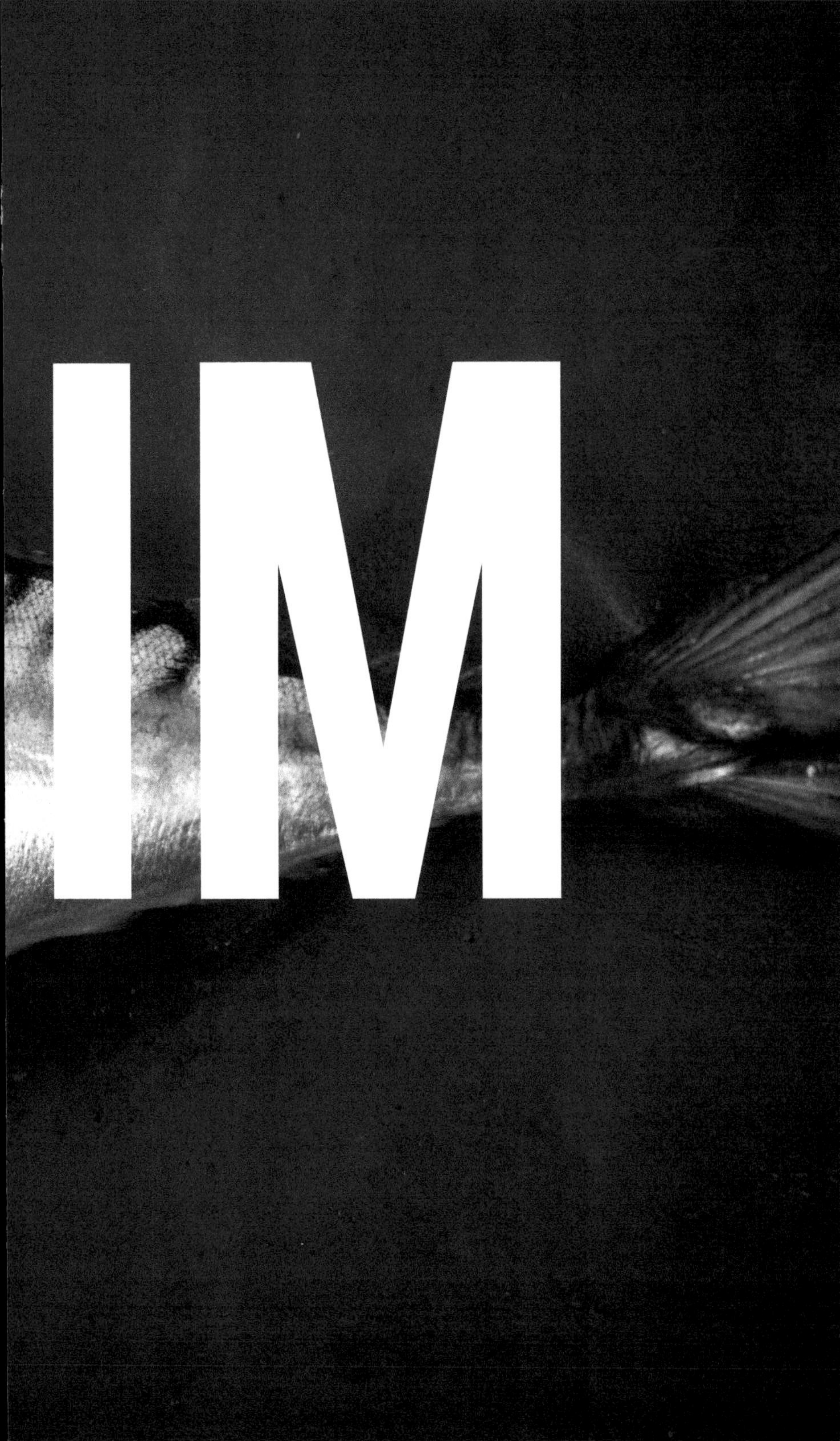
IM

- 1 Spring onion, chopped
- 1 Slice of smoked salmon
- 1 egg
- Handful of spinach

Method

1. Lay a piece of cling film over a cup or a ramekin, pushing the cling film into the hole.
2. Bung in the salmon and a couple of pieces of spinach, and then sprinkle in the spring onion.
3. Carefully crack in an egg. Bring the edges of the cling film together forming a ball and the salmon has encased the egg. Twist the clingfilm to tighten and then knot.
3. Throw this in a saucepan of boiling water for about 6 minutes.

SWIM

Salmon & Poached Egg Balls

Prawn Jambalaya

SWIM

Method

1. Heat the oil in a large, deep frying pan. Add the onion and celery, and fry for 5 minutes to soften. Add the rice and spices, and pour in the tomatoes with a can of water. Stir in the stock gel, pepper, garlic and thyme.
2. Cover and simmer for 30 minutes until rice is tender and most of the liquid has gone. Throw in the prawns and parsley, then stir and heat through for 5 minutes. Enjoy.

- 1 tbsp oil
- 1 onion, chopped
- 3 celery sticks, sliced
- 100g wholegrain basmati rice
- 1 tsp mild chilli powder
- 1 tbsp ground coriander
- tsp fennel seeds
- 1 tin of chopped tomatoes
- 1 stock gel
- 1 yellow pepper, roughly chopped
- 2 garlic cloves, chopped
- 1 tbsp thyme
- 150g pack of fresh prawns
- Good rip of parsley, chopped

LUNGE

Stand with your hands on your hips, with your feet a hip-width apart. Step your right leg forwards and slowly lower your body until your left (back) knee is close to, or touching, the floor and bent at least 90 degrees. Return to the starting position and repeat on the other side

"NO MATTER HOW YOU FEEL, GET UP, DRESS UP, SHOW UP AND NEVER GIVE UP"

LOWER
BODY

SQUAT

Stand with your feet parallel or turned out at 15 degrees – whichever is most comfortable. Slowly start to crouch by bending your hips and knees until your thighs are, at least, parallel to the floor. Make sure your heels do not rise off the floor. Press through your heels to return to a standing position.

Jack Nolan

Author, twenty one years old

WHAT IS YOUR EXPERIENCE WITH MENTAL ILLNESS?

My mental health breakdown happened in February 2016 when I suffered a psychosis episode. I was incredibly stressed with university, voluntary work and my personal relationships. I was trying to please everyone around me, instead of looking after myself.

I started to become eccentric, manic and showing symptoms of psychosis. I had an idea to create a platform for creative people and became unstoppable with this idea, contacting people in the middle of the night and thus getting no sleep. All I could think about was pushing my idea forward. I let the idea take over and spent a couple of weeks not sleeping, unbeknown to my family. I was networking hard and fast, which led to me crashing.

One particular morning, I went into my parents' room very early fully dressed in smart clothes and said that I had an important meeting. My parents asked me what was going on and tried to get me to talk. I broke down and when I tried to talk, no words of sense came out. I felt like I had lost all sense of reality and began to get paranoid and delusional thoughts. I thought I was getting messages through the television and felt that God was sending me specific instructions. The message from God was to save the world and become a leader, and to get people to do good things. Then, paranoia set in and I believed someone wanted to hurt me and my family. I began to say that people would have to die if they didn't follow me.

I was quite clearly having a mental breakdown and went into hospital to see the experts.

In the hospital, several psychiatrists assessed me to see if I needed to be sectioned or not. I didn't trust them and thought they were the 'bad guys'. I insulted and threatened them. I was completely manic by this stage and constantly spoke for more than ten hours, until I was finally given some medication to calm myself down. Thankfully, I fell asleep. It was agreed that I would be sectioned, which was the most heartbreaking news my parents would ever have to hear. I had no idea where I was, who I was or what was happening. I now remember very little about what happened in the hospital and only certain parts stick in my mind.

I do not remember my family coming to see me. I was in the hospital for nineteen days and the first two weeks, I felt that I was in a different world. I felt that all the people in the hospital were there for a reason and that they had a special gift – it was like the X-Men!

I finally realised where I was when, one day, while sitting on the sofa, I heard one of the patients on the phone ordering a pizza, shouting, "Deliver it to the mental institution." As soon as I heard this, the penny dropped. Until then, I hadn't realised where I was and I didn't know whether I had died and gone to heaven.

I had been given a mobile phone and instantly called my parents, freaking out and screaming, "Mum, I cannot believe you've put me in this place!" It was a scary environment. My defences went up and I started to vandalise the environment because I was scared of what was going on. I destroyed any object I felt could be a threat to me. The doctors discussed that I may have to stay in the hospital for a long time as the medication didn't seem to be bringing me down. It was an unnerving time and I knew I needed to get out. The environment was not helping.

In the third week of being in the hospital, my Mum and Dad seemed to be getting through to me. They gave me lots of positive support. I needed to stay as calm as possible and not upset the other patients. I also had a very mischievous side to me and would often play jokes on the patients, which was not always to their liking. I eventually started to support the others in the unit in a very positive way. There were many young people who were trying to take their own lives and you could often hear screams in the night. There were very serious mental health issues and I knew it wasn't right that I was there, even though I did help and inspire a lot of the patients. I was liked by the patients and the staff, and was known as the cheeky, happy–go-lucky guy – well, when I wasn't vandalising the place, that is. It was the first time I had been away from my parents and I felt I needed to become a more positive person. I felt that I could save the others and if I did, I could also save myself.

My parents started to push the doctors to get me out of the unit as they felt that I would get better support in a more positive way at home. I similarly felt that I wouldn't improve while in the hospital and that I wouldn't get back to being myself if I stayed any longer.

My mum and dad visited every day from opening time to closing time for nineteen days. Other members of the family also visited, as my parents felt I needed constant support to get me through my illness. Eventually, after appealing, and I was allowed home for one night, the doctors agreed it would be best for me to be discharged.

It was not easy at home. I had to relearn how to count and the alphabet. I was very emotional and was unable to sleep alone for the first few weeks. It seemed that recovery was going to be a long and slow process, and would be done in my own time. I was given three years of support from the Intervention Team.

After a few months of trying to get back on track, I had another breakdown, though it was not as severe. My girlfriend of five years split up with me; she couldn't handle the situation and it was too much for her. I completely understood, as I had changed as a person – looking back, it was for the best. In my recovery, I couldn't have long conversations or be very social. I had to relearn how to hold a conversation and other basic things in life. Showing certain emotions was a struggle. One of the happiest moments for my mum was when she heard me singing in the shower. It was something so simple, but it was a mammoth step in the right direction. A few months later, my uncle helped me to get back into the gym. I started slowly by walking on the treadmill and lifting a few weights. I feel that exercise has helped a lot with my recovery.

Now, I try to always remember what one doctor once told me, "Don't try and rush things, Jack. It will be a long process. The only way I can describe what has happened to your brain is by comparing it with being hit by a 10-tonne truck." This statement really is something to think about.

WHAT DO YOU DO TO KEEP YOURSELF ON A STEADY LEVEL?

I feel that a healthy body gives me a healthy mind. I have never really been a big drinker, but I have become very aware of what the impact of alcohol has on my body and so I try to refrain from drinking regularly. I am very conscious of the medication I take and alcohol make it worse for me. I stick to a routine of exercise and have become more aware of what my body needs. I now know sleep is incredibly important for me to have a balanced mental health.

I try not to get overexcited or to overthink new things. I have put a focus on being much more self-aware and on being a more relaxed version of myself. I now feel more mature and that I can deal with so much more with a calmer attitude. I see a social worker every four to six weeks to make sure I am progressing well.

Some doctors believe that I have bipolar and others believe it could just be a one-off episode – hopefully, this is the case. I don't feel that a diagnosis will make any difference to me. I have to decide whether to accept someone's opinion or to carry on as I already do, and accept that I am who I am. Everyone's normal is different.

WHAT'S YOUR FAVOURITE FOOD?

I love chicken. My favourite is Nando's and I often make a similar version at home.

"Everyone's normal is different"

-Jack Nolan

WALL SIT

LOWER BODY

Who needs a chair when there's a wall?

Slowly slide your back down a wall until your thighs are parallel to the ground.

Make sure your knees are directly above your ankles and keep your back straight.

Difficult roads often lead to beautiful destinations

Method

1. Bung the sushi rice into boiling water and simmer with lid on for 10 minutes until cooked. Drain and set aside. Fluff up with a fork and bung in the sushi vinegar and mix.
2. Chop the vegetables into small strips. Feel free to use any vegetables you want.
3. Once cool, lay a sheet of nori on top of a bamboo sushi mat, shiny side down. Fill a clean bowl with cold water to wet your fingers before handling the rice. Grab a handful of rice and press down onto nori sheets, making sure you cover it all but leaving a clear strip furthest away from you. Bung in the ingredients in a strip (I matched salmon with carrots and cucumber, and prawns with avocado, but do what you fancy).
4. Using the bamboo mat to help, roll the sushi up tightly, rolling it away from you towards the strip of clear nori. Once you get to the end, wet the clear strip to seal the roll. Job done!
5. Most supermarkets have sushi-making kits, which are ideal for first-timers.

- 250g sushi rice
- 3 tbsp sushi vinegar
- 1 Carrot
- 1 Cucumber
- 1 Avocado
- Handful of cooked prawns
- 2 Slices of smoked salmon
- 3 sheets of nori (dried seaweed)
- Soy sauce to serve (optional)

Sushi
SWIM

Salmon & Pasta

SWIM

Method

1. Marinade the salmon with the onion, parsley, a glug of oil and a squeeze of lemon.
2. Cook your pasta. While it's boiling, glug in some oil to the pan and bung in your breadcrumbs to toast off. Once done, tip out onto kitchen roll.
3. Glug in a little bit more oil and fry off the salmon. One minute later, bung in the tomatoes and spring onion, and cook for a further 2 minutes until the salmon is cooked. Drain the pasta and add it to the pan. Give it a good mix.
4. Once you have plated everything up, sprinkle the breadcrumbs and basil

- Salmon fillet, cut into strips
- 3 tbsp breadcrumbs
- 5 tbsp olive oil
- 1 tbsp lemon juice
- 1 onion
- Good handful of fresh parsley, finely chopped
- 2 spring onions
- Tin of plum tomatoes.
- Bowl of flat pasta
- Good twist of salt and pepper
- Fresh basil, chopped

Courgetti Spaghetti & Prawns

SWIM

- 1 pack of prawns
- 3 garlic cloves, crushed
- Pinch of chilli flakes, or more if you like a tingle
- ¼ cup chicken stock
- Juice of 1 lemon
- Twist of salt and pepper
- 4 courgettes, spiralised
- 2 tbsp Parmesan, grated
- Big rip of parsley, chopped
- Glug of oil

Method

1. Grab a pan, glug in the oil and place over a medium heat. Throw in the prawns, garlic and chilli. Cook until prawns are pink.
2. Pour in the chicken stock and squeeze the lemon. Bring to a simmer and bung in the courgetti spaghetti. Mix together for a couple of minutes.
3. Serve and add Parmesan and parsley if you fancy.

- 3–4 new potatoes, halved
- 1 fillet of white fish (cod / Vietnamese River Cobbler)
- Handful of spinach
- 1 red pepper, sliced
- Twist of fresh parsley
- A slice of lemon
- Splash of white wine

Fish Meal in a Bag

SWIM

Method

1. Bring a pan to boil and par cook new potatoes. Preheat oven to 180ºC.
2. Make a bag out of tin foil and throw in the spuds, spinach and pepper. Place on top the fish with the lemon and parsley. Splash with wine and season.
3. Bung in the oven for around 15–20 minutes. Winner, winner, fish-in-a-bag dinner!

QUADRUPED LEG LIFT

Starting on your hands and knees, keep a flat back and engage your core. Raise your left leg straight back, stopping when your foot is at hip-level and your thigh is parallel to the floor. Balance for as long as possible, then raise your bottom right knee off the floor, tightening your butt, back and abs (try to be graceful here!). Hold for three seconds, then switch legs.

LOWER BODY

SINGLE LEG DEADLIFT

Start in a standing position with your feet together. Lift your right leg slightly, and lower your arms and torso while raising your right leg behind your body. Keep your left knee slightly bent and reach your arms as close to the floor as possible. Raise your torso while lowering your right leg. Switch legs.

Jonny Benjamin and Neil Laybourn

Mental Health Advocates

WHAT ARE YOUR EXPERIENCES WITH MENTAL ILLNESS?

Neil's story:

My experience with mental health came out of the blue. I was twenty-four and I was walking to work when I met Jonny on Waterloo Bridge in London. Jonny was in a bad way and considering taking his own life, but I didn't realise this straightaway. Jonny told me that he was considering taking his own life and we spoke together for a while. I kept him talking until the police came after twenty-five minutes or so and Johnny was taken to hospital. This was the first conversation I had ever had with anyone around the subject of suicide. It got the cogs turning for me and I spoke to my girlfriend (now my wife) about it.

Six years later, Jonny started a campaign to find the stranger who had helped him on the bridge. The campaign was called 'The Stranger on the Bridge'. Within three months, the story had garnered an unprecedented amount of media and reached 300 million people worldwide. As a result, the we were reunited. Since then, we have started on a fabulous journey together and are now ambassadors for Rethink Mental Illness.

The journey has evolved at a fast pace. I have learnt about the landscape of mental health in the UK, travelling the country and talking widely about it. I have learnt that suicide is the biggest killer of men under forty-five in the UK. In the first twenty-four years of my life, I had only had one conversation about mental health and suicide, with Jonny. But in just a short time after we started working together, I had spoken to hundreds of people about suicide. I tried to take something away from each conversation and use it in my own life. I want the stigma to end. I want the conversation about mental health to be open and honest.

Jonny's story:

When I was twenty, I was diagnosed with schizoaffective disorder, which is a combination of schizophrenia and bipolar. I had been ill for a while before the incident on the bridge, but I hadn't known how to deal with it or how to handle it. I was embarrassed and ashamed, and didn't have the words to explain how I felt. The diagnosis made me feel that my world had ended. It seemed impossible to me that I would get any better and I felt that I was labelled for life. There was so much negativity in the media about schizophrenia. I had never read anything positive about the condition. I went to hospital for a month and made a decision that it was better for everyone that I wasn't around.

So, I went to the bridge. I don't know how long I was there for before Neil came along and we had our conversation. Neil listened very patiently and very empathetically. I hadn't been listened to before and the main thing Neil said was that he thought I would be fine.

Never before had anyone told me that they thought I would be okay. After the conversation, I was taken away by the police, sectioned and it took a long time to recover. I don't feel like I will ever recover, but I have found that the best thing for me is talking about it.

I then launched the campaign to find Neil. Since then, life has been busy and we've visited schools, business and prisons to talk about mental health. I want to remove the embarrassment and shame surrounding mental illness. My biggest passion is to get mental health awareness embedded into the school curriculum. It is a worrying fact that 75 per cent of mental health issues begin in adolescence and yet mental health is not part of the curriculum.

To date, I still have relapses and still struggle, but I now asks for help and makes sure to get it.

WHAT DO YOU DO TO KEEP YOURSELF ON A STEADY LEVEL?

I (Jonny) believe in talking about mental illness openly and that going into detail about your thoughts and opening up about them will help you. A lot of the stigma surrounding mental health is due to embarrassment and paranoia. I see a therapist and psychiatrist. I have also tried mindfulness, which has helped me. It has taught me about self-acceptance and self-forgiveness. A big part of my journey towards recovery is that I have learnt to be kinder to myself.

I (Neil) have noticed that when talking in public about mental health, it is easier to open up to a stranger to share an experience than seeing a therapist. I feel that talking to people is a therapeutic process. I also like to have barriers in my everyday life. So, for example, I won't respond to emails after dinner and I go to bed early to get my eight hours' sleep. I eat healthily and exercise. I let myself have guilty pleasures and try not to beat myself up if I fall off the wagon. Having some self-compassion is also important. I have two chickens and I love looking after them, as it gives me good endorphins. Having something to look after and nurture helps me – Betty and Margot, my chickens, keep me in line!

WHAT'S YOUR FAVOURITE FOOD?

My (Jonny's) favourite food is chicken (much to the annoyance of Neil!). When I have chicken, I saves the bones and everything else and makes a good stock from it. I then use the stock and adds fresh vegetables, noodles and chicken. I call it 'Jewish penicillin'!

My (Neil's) favourite food is French food, such as beef bourguignon. I also love cooking.

PRAWN, SPUDS & CHORIZO

SWIM

- 250G NEW POTATOES, COOKED AND QUARTERED
- 1 RED CHILLI, FINELY CHOPPED WITH SEEDS
- 4 GARLIC CLOVES, FINELY SLICED
- 1 TIN OF CHOPPED PLUM TOMATOES
- 350 G RAW KING PRAWNS
- 1 HANDFUL OF FRESH PARSLEY, CHOPPED
- GOOD TWIST OF SALT AND PEPPER

Method

1. Heat a medium frying pan on a medium heat, then bung in the chorizo and fry for 2–3 minutes until slightly crispy on each side. Remove the chorizo from the pan and soak up fat on a piece of kitchen roll. Fry the new potatoes until golden brown.

2. Add the chorizo back into the pan, then stir in the chilli and garlic and sauté for a further 2 minutes. Give it a good toss and stir.

3. Add the tomatoes and bring to the boil, then add the prawns and simmer for 5–10 minutes until the tomatoes have thickened and the prawns are cooked through. Sprinkle over the parsley.
Bish, bash, bosh!

COD & CHORIZO
SWIM

- 4 large cod fillets
- Lots of cherry tomatoes, halved (I used red, green and yellow)
- 1 can of chickpeas
- Half a chorizo ring, sliced
- 4 garlic cloves, peeled
- 2 red onions, sliced
- 2 bell peppers
- Good pinch of flat-leaf parsley, roughly chopped
- ½ tsp sweet paprika
- Splash of white wine
- ½ a lemon
- Salt and freshly ground pepper to season

Method

1. Preheat oven to 200°C. Finely chop the chorizo and garlic. Grab a large roasting tray, splash a bit of oil in it and spread in the chickpeas, pepper, onions and tomatoes. Sprinkle on half of the chorizo and garlic and bang in the oven for 10 minutes.

2. Take out the tray and glug in a bit of wine. Then, place the vegetables and cod on top, and rub in the remainder of the chorizo and garlic mixture.
3. Bung in the oven for around 15–20 minutes or until the fish is cooked. Squeeze on the lemon juice, lob on the parsley and serve.

PRAWN & COD FISHCAKES

SWIM

- 2 good sized potatoes
- Handful of rocket
- 1 cup of frozen peas, defrosted
- 1 bag of raw prawns, peeled and chopped
- Finely grated zest and juice of 1 lemon
- 1 large egg, beaten
- Small bunch of fresh chives, snipped
- 2 boneless and skinless cod fillets
- Plain flour for dusting
- Splash of olive oil

Method

1. Boil the potatoes for 15 minutes until tender. Chuck in a bowl and mash. Allow to cool and then throw in the prawns, peas, lemon zest, egg and a twist of salt and pepper. Mix together.
2. While potatoes are cooling, half fill a saucepan with water and poach the cod for 5–8 minutes until the fish is cooked. Place on the side and pat dry with kitchen roll. Flake the fish, drop in the bowl and mix.
3. With your hands, pick up the mixture and mould into patties. Heat up a large frying pan, drop in some oil and fry the patties for 3–4 minutes on either side.

Salmon Boat

SWIM

Method

1. Preheat oven to 200°C.
2. Oil and season the salmon and place it in foil. Fold up the sides, making a little boat to hold it in.
3. In a small bowl, bung in the honey, lime juice, chopped coriander and garlic. Mix and tip onto the salmon.
4. Leave the boat open-topped and bake for 15–20 minutes.
5. Remove salmon from the foil. The skin will stick to the foil, but don't worry. Once on a plate, spoon the juices left in the boat on the salmon.

- 1 salmon
- 1 glug of olive oil
- Twist of salt and pepper
- 2 tbsp honey
- Freshly squeezed lime juice
- Handful of coriander, chopped
- 3 garlic cloves, minced

NOTES

NOTES

GOAL SETTING

When Stu was diagnosed with depression, he tried to think of things that could help him through the day and months. From his days as a salesman and a primary school teacher, he used to follow the 'SMART' goal:

S - SPECIFIC, SIGNIFICANT, STRETCHING.
M - MEASURABLE, MEANINGFUL, MOTIVATIONAL.
A - AGREED UPON, ATTAINABLE, ACHIEVABLE, ACCEPTABLE.
R - REALISTIC, RELEVANT, REASONABLE.
T - TIME-BASED, TIME-BOUND, TIMELY, TANGIBLE.

From this, he set his goals, such as not drinking in the week, exercising a minimum of three times in the week and getting a minimum of five new clients a week. He set realistic targets and goals that would fit into his lifestyle and time.

Your goals can be anything from taking the stairs instead of the lift, cooking a homemade meal at least four times week and going for a walk every Sunday. Just make it SMART.

"Many people fail in life, not for lack of ability or brains or even courage, but simply because they have never organised their energies around a goal."

Elbert Hubbard, American philosopher and writer.

- Change can be scary, but if you start with smaller goals, following the SMART model, you are more likely to achieve them. You will feel a great sense of achievement, which will send positive messages to your brain about setting new goals.
- Write your goals down and pin them somewhere you can see them. This makes the goals real and they become a motivational tool. Studies have shown that people who write their goals down are 50 per cent more likely to achieve them. Writing your goals down also decreases ruminative thinking (ruminating is the process of thinking about the past over and over). A study in a German university showed that people had decreased levels of psychological stress and rumination when they wrote their goals down.
- Find an accountability partner. If you need help with sticking to your goals, find a friend who can hold you accountable in a positive, friendly and encouraging way.
- Visualise your goal. When you practise visualisation, your brain does not distinguish reality from fanciful imaginings. Neural pathways are created nonetheless, so your brain will act as if this is a habit. Your goal will become a habit, which will then become achievable.
- When you have achieved your goal, shout about it! Make sure you give yourself a pat on the back and tell yourself you've done well.

"WAKE UP WITH DETERMINATION; GO TO BED WITH SATISFACTION"

TO SLEEP OR NOT TO SLEEP?

A lack of sleep or too much sleep has been linked to mental health. Sleep is crucial for our bodies to recuperate and for the brain to consolidate all of the information and experiences from the day. Every person we interviewed for this book spoke about the impact of the lack of sleep on their mental health.

Being able to sleep and helping the body to relax is very much linked to how much you exercise and what you eat and drink.

Sleep is a lot more complex than we think and it is very important for staying healthy. Indeed, there is a strong link between sleep and health. The lack of sleep has a huge impact on people's lives and has consequences for mental health

The Great British Sleep Survey found that poor sleep had a negative impact on people's lives and severe consequences for mental health. People who are feeling low in their mood have less energy to exercise, less energy to take the time to cook healthily and are more likely to develop mental health problems. Sleep is as important to our health as eating, drinking and breathing.

"Your
only limit
is you"

SOME ALARMING FACTS ABOUT SLEEP INCLUDE:

- Nearly half of us are getting just six hours or less sleep at night.
- A bed may deteriorate by as much as 70 per cent from its new state after ten years.
- You need at least six hours of sleep a night to recharge your batteries and to learn new things the next day, scientists have claimed.
- Some scientists say that people who do not get enough sleep are more likely to have bigger appetites due to the fact that their leptin levels fall and increase appetite (leptin is an appetite-regulating hormone).
- The less sleep you have, the more likely you are to get ill, because your body cannot fight off the bugs.
  - Lack of sleep can decrease your immune system, libido, fertility and weight gain.

Alicia Benbow is a Life Coach using several therapies such as NLP, EMDR and CBT

Sleep is an essential part of our wellbeing. Without it, we become tired, agitated and unable to focus. Over a prolonged period of time, lack of sleep can lead to anxiety, depression and other serious illnesses such as heart disease, high blood pressure, diabetes and strokes.

While we sleep, our brains recover, repair and prepare. It processes relevant information it has taken in, clears out the 'waste' and ensures our body runs efficiently by regulating our system, which, in turn, boosts our overall immunity.

Tests show that people with reduced sleep levels have less activity in their parietal lobes, which are responsible for decision-making, problem-solving and memory. They also show, among other things, reduced levels of leptin (the chemical that makes you feel full) and increased levels of ghrelin (a hunger-stimulating hormone), which can lead to obesity issues.

TIPS FOR BETTER SLEEP

Warm bath (not hot) – at a comfortable resting body temperature

Gentle (not vigorous) exercise – yoga stretches

Relaxation – breathing exercises

CDs – gentle music

Reading a book

To do lists – to organise thoughts

Listing positives from the day

Imagine waking up, having had a relaxing night's sleep

Focus on what you want and what you don't want

Turn electronic devices off

Sleep in a dark, tidy room, with a temperature of approximately 18 degrees.

Keep your bedroom for sleep (and sex – which promotes good sleep!)

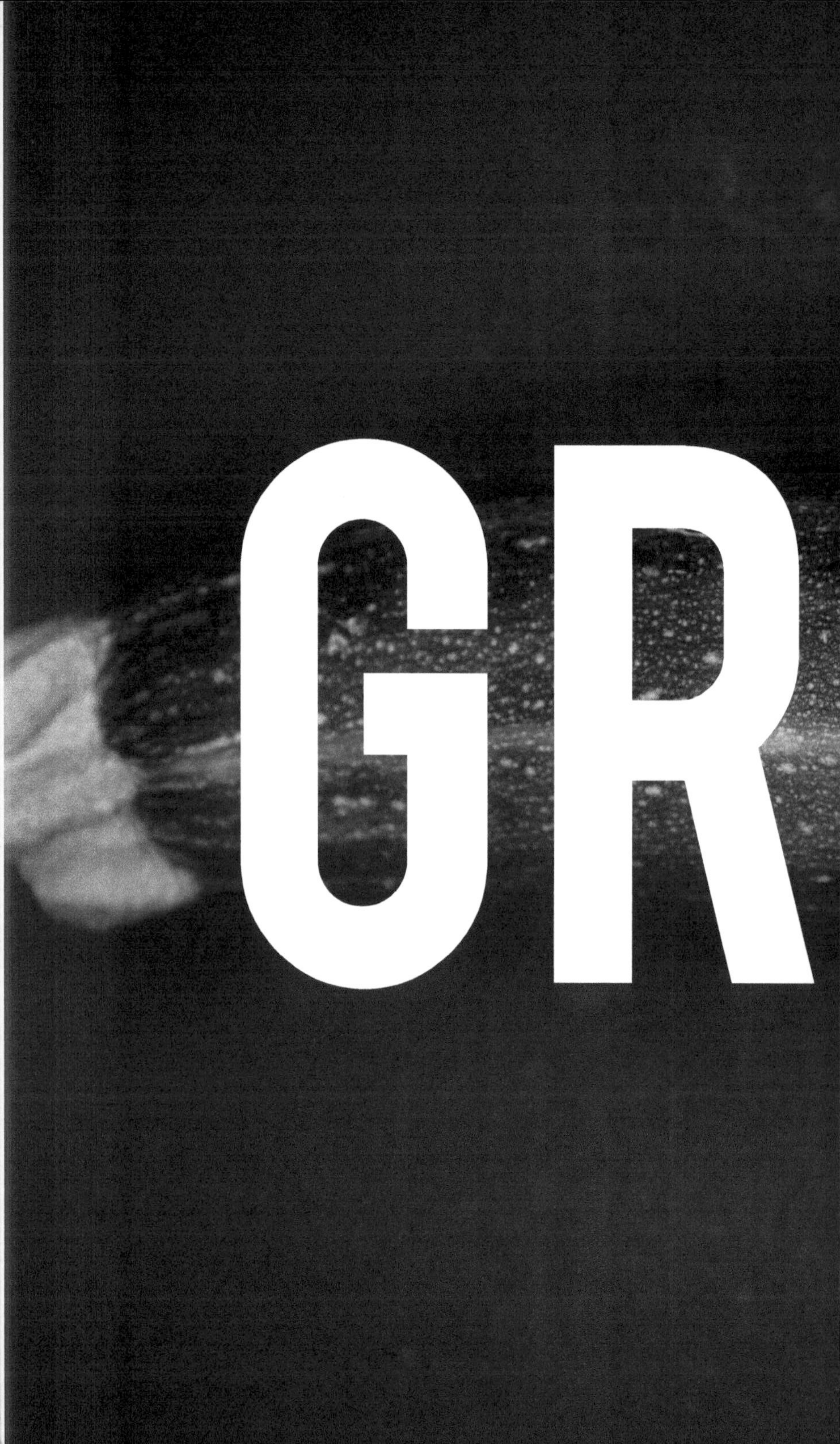
GR

OW

Method

1. Working over the sink, wrap the grated beetroot in a clean
   J-cloth and squeeze out as much liquid as possible, then
   bung in a large bowl. Add spring onions, garlic, mint, lemon
   zest, a squeeze of lemon juice, 2 tbsp of the flour and the
   egg, along with a good twist of salt and pepper. When well
   mixed, stir in the feta.
2. Form the mixture into burger-shaped patties and coat with
   the remaining flour. Heat a large frying pan over a medium-
   high heat with a good glug of olive oil and fry the patties
   for 4-5 minutes on each side until crisp on the outside and
   cooked. Be careful of your white T-shirt with the beetroot

Beetroot & Feta Burger

GROW

- 4 bulbs of raw beetroot, peeled and coarsely grated
- Small bunch of spring onions, finely chopped
- 2 garlic cloves, crushed
- Small bunch of fresh mint, chopped
- Finely grated zest and juice of 1 lemon
- 3 tbsp plain flour
- 1 medium egg
- Pck of feta, crumbled
- Good glug of olive oil

Paste:
- 4 hot red chillies
- 6 garlic cloves
- 5cm ginger, peeled and roughly sliced
- 4 tbsp coriander stalks, chopped
- 2 lemongrass stalks, white inner part only, roughly chopped
- 2 small shallots, roughly chopped
- ½ tsp ground coriander
- 1½ tsp turmeric
- 1 tsp curry powder

The rest:
- 3 packets of fresh noodles
- ½ head of broccoli, divided into florets
- ½ butternut squash, peeled and diced
- A large handful of flat green beans, cut on the diagonal
- A glug of oil
- 750 ml vegetable stock
- 250 ml coconut milk
- 3 tbsp soy sauce
- Juice of ½ lime

Khao Soi Soup

Method

1. Bung all of the paste ingredients into a food processor with around 4 tbsp of water and blitz until you make a paste.

2. Glug the oil in a medium-sized pot. Add Khao Soi paste to the hot oil and stir-fry for about 5 minutes. Pour in the vegetable broth and coconut milk and allow them to come to the boil. Season with soy sauce, a squeeze of lime and sugar to taste.

3. Bung the diced butternut squash into the soup, allow the soup to come to the boil and simmer for about 7 minutes. Add broccoli florets, sliced beans and noodles, and cook for a further 5 minutes.

4. Pour into bowls and serve with fresh coriander.

GROW

ABS

BICYCLE

- Lie down with your knees bent and your hands behind your head.

- With your knees in towards your chest, bring your right elbow towards your left knee as your right leg straightens.

- Continue alternating sides as though you're pedalling. Just keep the helmet in the closet!

Step 1:

Step 2:

CRUNCH

Step 1:

Step 2:

Before anyone's crowned Captain Crunch, remember form is key!

- Lie on your back with the knees bent and feet flat on the floor.

- With hands placed on your thighs peel the head and shoulders off the mat while engaging the core sliding your hands towards the knees.

- Continue curling up until the upper back is off the mat.

- Hold briefly, then lower the torso back toward the mat slowly.

Asparagus and Tomato Frittata

Method

1. Warm up the oven to 180°C and grease a baking tin.

2. In a pan, warm up a glug of oil and bung in the carrots, onion and red pepper until soft. Then, throw in the asparagus and spinach for another couple of minutes. Tip into the baking tray and spread out with the tomatoes.

3. Pour in the beaten eggs and throw in the oven for about 25 minutes. Great for your lunchbox!

- 6 eggs
- Twist of salt and pepper
- Asparagus (about 5 stalks)
- Glug of oil
- 1 small onion
- 1 Carrot, grated
- 1 Red pepper, diced
- Handful of spinach
- Handful of cherry tomatoes

"CAN AND I WILL"

"PROVE THEM WRONG"

"CREATE YOUR OWN SUNSHINE"

NOTES

GROW

Megan Jones

Multimedia News and
Sports Reporter
Free Radio

WHAT IS YOUR EXPERIENCE WITH MENTAL ILLNESS?

I was a student and went out for a meal one night, then continued onto a bar afterwards. I used to work in a bar myself, so I was very conscious of groups of people messing around and causing trouble. I mentioned to the bar staff that they should clear a particular group away as people couldn't even get to the ladies. Someone from the group overheard my conversation and I heard them say, "Snitches get stitches." I thought the comment was odd, but got back to my friends in a table in the corner. We laughed and talked a bit about the odd comment. All of a sudden, I felt people gathering around me and a man dropped a drink down my back. I stood up and asked him what he was doing. One of the lads was holding a glass with a handle and he threw it at me, launching at my head. I can't remember much from there on. I can remember telling my friends to get me outside, but the next thing I remember is waking up in the recovery position on the pavement, covered in blood.

The ambulance came and I was taken to hospital. A long path of facial plastic surgery followed. I gave a police statement and they eventually found the man who had thrown the glass at me. He was out on license. I didn't know him. The man got four years and served two of those years. I couldn't leave my house after the incident. I had a huge breakdown in the middle of a shopping centre, as I was so scared of being outside.

I had an MRI after the attack and they found fluid on my brain. I was diagnosed with PTSD and depression after the incident. I continue to have memory loss and sees a neurophysiologist every six months. I was supposed to go to Rome a week after the attack, but on the morning of the day I was supposed to go, my stitches burst open and they found a lot more glass in my face.

I see a councillor every week to talk about what had happened to me. I have found that I have become a lot more anxious. If I am not in control of a situation, I can feel the anxiety building. I feel I have changed and I don't go out as much as I used to.

WHAT DO YOU DO TO KEEP YOURSELF ON A STEADY LEVEL?

I went to the cafe at my mum's gym one day. A personal trainer came up to me and asked if I wanted to do some boxing, in order to channel the energy. I did. It made me more confident and I have found I could get rid of the bad energy and focus in on exercise. I now attend the gym in the morning and it makes my whole day better. It seems to focus my mind and channel my anger in the right way, and I don't feel as scared as much as I used to. After starting the gym sessions, healthy eating came naturally and made me feel better.

WHAT IS YOUR FAVOURITE FOOD?

My favourite at the moment is a chocolate mousse made with avocado, dates, cocoa powder, protein powder and a little bit of milk. Blend it all together and stick a few raspberries on the top. If you stick it in a small pot and then in the freezer, it's totally like a professional mousse!

BBQ CHILLI VEGETABLES

GROW

- 1 Broccoli
- 1 Cauliflower
- 1 Bottle of sweet chilli sauce
- Glug of oil
- Twist of salt and pepper

Method

1. Snap off all the florets of cauliflower and broccoli and slice into medallions. Then, hit with a twist of salt and pepper and a glug of oil. Mix and bung on a griddle or barbeque.

2. Cook until soft and chargrilled and throw in the chilli sauce. Mix and continue to cook until it turns into a sticky mess.

Method

1. In a bowl, whisk up the soy sauce, sesame oil, sugar and mirin, and leave to the side.

2. Glug oil in wok and bung in pepper, snap peas and carrots. Stir-fry until soft and throw in the garlic.

3. Stir in the sauce and noodles and toss to combine, stir-frying for another 3 minutes.

4. If you're feeling a bit meaty, throw in cooked prawns or chicken in between points 2 and 3.

- 1 packet of fresh to wok noodles
- Glug of oil
- 1 red bell pepper, julienned
- 1 carrot, julienned
- Handful of sugar snap peas
- 3 cloves of garlic, minced
- 3 tbsp low sodium soy sauce and mirin
- 1 tsp sesame oil and sugar

VEGETABLE STIR FRY

VEGGIE PAKORA

- Cauliflower, cut into bite-sized pieces
- 1 red onion, roughly chopped
- 1 handful of new potatoes
- Twist of salt and pepper
- 1 pinch of cayenne pepper
- 1 tsp garam masa
- 1 tsp curry powd
- 2 garlic cloves, minced
- Handful of corian chopped
- 225g chickpea / gram flour
- 250ml water
- Glug of oil

Method

1. Preheat oven to 260°C.
2. Grab a large mixing bowl and throw in all of vegetables, spices and coriander.
3. In another bowl, mix the flour and water i a batter-like mixture. Pour in the bowl vegetables and toss.
4. Line a baking tray with baking paper and th in the vegetables, making sure they are overlapping.
5. Bung in the oven and bake for 12 minu turning halfway through.
6. This recipe is great with a bit of mango chutr

- 300g carrot, grated
- 100g cheddar cheese, grated
- 2 eggs
- 3 tbsp gluten-free oat flour
- Twist of salt and pepper

Method

1. Grate the carrots. Bung them into a bowl and cover with water. Microwave for 5 minutes.
2. Firmly squeeze out the water from the carrots and place in a paper towel to dry. Make sure they are very dry and bung them in a bowl with eggs, flour, salt and pepper. Give it a good old mix.
3. Grab a baking tray and line with baking paper. Dollop a spoonful of mixture onto the tray and, using fingers, press it down, making a circle.
4. Bake at 200°C for 15 minutes or until crispy on the sides.
5. Remove from oven and place over a bottle to form a taco shape. Fill with your choice of filling. These are also great with chilli con carnie.

CARROT TACOS

GROW

METHOD

1. In a large saucepan, heat the oil over a medium heat. Bung in the onions and fry until soft.
2. Add the garlic, paprika and bay leaves and fry for a further minute.
3. Bung in everything else and season. Simmer for 15 minutes. As it finishes, stir the spinach through to wilt.

A glug of olive oil
1 onion, diced
2 garlic cloves, finely chopped
1 tsp sweet smoked paprika
2 bay leaves
2 tins of butter beans, drained and rinsed
2 tins of plum tomatoes
A twist of sea salt and black pepper
2 large handfuls of spinach, roughly chopped

TOMATO - HALLOUMI BAKE

- Glug of vegetable oil
- 1 onion, chopped
- 2 cloves of garlic, chopped
- 2 courgettes, chopped
- 6 medium tomatoes, chopped
- 1 tbsp tomato puree,
- turmeric, cumin, smoked paprika, chilli flakes
- Good twist of salt and pepper
- 200g halloumi, sliced
- Handful of fresh basil, chopped

METHOD

1. Glug the oil in a frying pan. Bung in the onion and garlic and fry until soft.
2. Throw in the tomatoes and courgettes, then the tomato puree and all of the spices, along with a good twist of salt and pepper. Cook over a medium heat for 20 minutes, until everything is softened and the tomatoes have released their liquid.
3. Place the slices of halloumi across the top of the vegetables. Slide under the grill for a few minutes until the cheese has

- 1 CUP OF QUINOA
- GOOD HANDFUL OF GREEN LEAVES
- ½ LARGE AVOCADO, SLICED
- SMALL WEDGE OF RED CABBAGE, SHREDDED THINLY
- 1 BROCCOLI, DIVIDED INTO FLORETS
- A HANDFUL OF FROZEN PEAS
- 1 SMALL CUCUMBER, SLICED
- A HANDFUL OF MUNG BEAN SPROUTS (OR OTHER SPROUTS)
- 1 COURGETTE
- 1 LARGE SPRING ONION, SLICED THINLY
- 10 GREEN OLIVES, PITTED AND QUARTERED
- A HANDFUL OF MINT AND BASIL LEAVES, CHOPPED FINELY

DRESSING:

- 3 TBSP EXTRA VIRGIN OLIVE OIL AND LEMON JUICE
- 1 GARLIC CLOVE, FINELY GRATED
- A PINCH OF CHILLI FLAKES
- GOOD TWIST OF SALT AND PEPPER

METHOD

1. COOK THE QUINOA AND LEAVE TO ONE SIDE. IN A PAN OF BOILING WATER, THROW THE BROCCOLI AND PEAS IN AND COOK FOR A MAX OF 2 MINUTES. AS SOON AS THEY COME OUT OF THE BOILING WATER, THROW INTO COLD WATER. SLICE THE COURGETTE AND COOK ON A HOT GRIDDLE PAN UNTIL BROWN ON EACH SIDE AND PLACE TO ONE SIDE.
2. IN A BOWL, MIX ALL OF THE DRESSING INGREDIENTS AND MIX
3. IN A LARGE SALAD BOWL, MIX ALL INGREDIENTS TOGETHER AND DRIZZLE OVER THE DRESSING.

QUINOA SUPERFOOD
SALAD

GROW

Asparagus Mushroom Pasta

- 250g pasta
- 6 asparagus, roughly chopped
- Glug of olive oil
- 2 good handfuls of mushrooms, sliced
- 4 spring onions, sliced
- 1 garlic, crushed
- 4 tbsp orange juice
- 200ml vegetable stock
- 200ml double cream
- Mozzarella Ball, shredded
- Good twist of salt and black pepper
- Handful of chopped coriander

Method

1 Cook the pasta and add the asparagus to the boiling water in the last 4 minutes. Drain and set aside.

2 Glug the olive oil in a frying pan and cook the mushrooms for about 10 minutes until soft. Bung in the spring onions and garlic, and cook for a couple more minutes.

3 Reduce the heat to low, pour in the stock and the cream, and give it a good mix. Bring to a simmer before adding in the cheese and coriander and mix until melted. Once melted, bung in the pasta and asparagus.

GROW

SPANISH TORTILLA

GROW

- 2 large onions, sliced
- Glug of oil
- 4 sweet potatoes, peeled and cubed
- 2 cloves of garlic
- 8 eggs
- 1 bag of spinach

Method

1. Bung the spinach into a large colander and tip a kettle of boiling water over it. Drain and squeeze out any remaining water. Place to the side.
2. Glug the oil into a pan and throw in the onions. Cook until soft. Then, bung in the garlic and spuds. Cover and cook for about 15 minutes until the spuds are tender.
3. Pour in the beaten eggs and give it a good mix. Now, add the spinach and fold in.
4. Cover and cook for about 10 minutes until the sides are golden brown.
5. Run a palette knife around the sides to stop it from sticking. Slide out the tortilla onto a plate and flip back in pan to cook the other side. Cook for another 5-10 minutes until golden brown. Done!

Danny Sculthorpe

Rugby Player –
State of Mind Charity

WHAT IS YOUR EXPERIENCE WITH MENTAL ILLNESS?

I played professional rugby for ten years. In 2010, I signed a four-year deal with Bradford. I had two young children, my wife wasn't working and I was bringing home a good wage. About three weeks into the season, I prolapsed a disc lifting weights and had to have surgery. When I woke up from the surgery, all the pain had gone. However, a week later, I started to get bad pains in my back, which made me call my surgeon. I knew something wasn't right.

I went straight in for an MRI scan and it turned out that I had picked up an MRSA infection in the bottom of my spine. I had to spend three months in hospital on the strongest painkillers. I then had to have more surgery because of the damage the MRSA infection had done. They took out the bottom part of my spine and fused my back. I was thirty years old and should have been at the peak of my career. For the next four to five months, I would get out of bed in the morning, go to the couch and go back to bed. I couldn't even make it to the toilet. I couldn't do any school runs; I couldn't do anything with my two young children; and I couldn't help my wife cook or clean or do anything around the house.

One day, I got a phone call from my agent, telling me that my contract had ended. I lost my job and the family home. This is when my depression started, as I couldn't support my family. I couldn't get the thought of suicide out of my mind. I did the typical man thing and kept my depression to myself. I thought it would be a sign of weakness if I asked for help.

Within a couple of months, I found myself in my car with boxes of pills and a bottle of gin. I wanted to take my own life. However, for some reason, I didn't. I don't know what stopped me – whether it was my kids, my wife or my parents – but I went home and put the gin and the pills away. Still, I was angry that I hadn't taken my own life and continued to sit on the couch, snap at the kids and be horrible to my wife.

I was lucky that my family noticed a big change in my personality. I have a large, close family, who told me they knew something was wrong and made me open up to them. I told them about the suicidal thoughts and that I felt I had let them all down. Getting it all off my chest was a turning point. It felt like a release to talk about it.

I went to see my doctor and I was put onto antidepressants. But the biggest thing that saved my life was talking about my feelings and I saw a counsellor. As such, my advice is to talk to someone. If I hadn't talked to my family, I would have taken my own life, thereby ruining my kids' lives and my parents' lives. I believe we have to look out for each other. If you notice a personality change in a work colleague, friend or family member, ask them if they are okay and wait until you get a proper answer from them.

WHAT DO YOU DO TO KEEP YOURSELF ON A STEADY LEVEL?

Talking is very important. In addition, I believe that training and physical activity is a massive antidepressant. It makes me feel great after training. I exercise for my head.

WHAT IS YOUR FAVOURITE FOOD?

I love tuna pasta! A simple pasta with loads of chilli. I also like donor kebabs.

Poached Egg on 'Chillied' Avocado and Sweet Potato Toast

- 2 EGGS
- 1 AVOCADO
- 1 RED CHILLI
- 1 SWEET POTATO

METHOD

1. Grab a saucepan, fill it with water and get it boiling.
2. Cut sweet potato into slices of around 1cm thickness and stick in the toaster on a high setting. While that's toasting, grab a bowl and throw in the avocado and chopped chilli. Mash and mix this together with the back of a fork and add a good shake of salt and pepper.
3. Drop eggs into the boiling water and poach. Pull out the potato from the toaster, spread the avocado on top and place the poached egg on top of that. A 4-minute breakfast… done!
4. If you haven't any sweet potato. Don't worry just resort back to good old fashioned toast like we did.

Chickpea & Spinach Curry

GROW

- Glug of oil
- 1 large onion, finely chopped
- 1 tsp of garlic paste, ginger paste and cumin powder
- 3 tsp curry powder
- 2 tsp garam masala
- ½ tsp chilli powder
- 1 tsp turmeric
- 1 tin of chickpeas, drained
- 1 tin of chopped tomatoes
- 4 medium potatoes, cubed
- 500ml vegetable stock
- ½ tsp salt
- Massive handful of fresh spinach

Method

1. Heat oil in a large pan. Add the onion, garlic and ginger and cook until soft.
2. Throw in all of the spices and cook for a further minute.
3. Bung in chopped tomatoes, chickpeas, potatoes, salt and about half of the vegetable stock. Stir well and simmer gently for around 20 minutes or until the potatoes are cooked, adding more stock as needed.
4. Add the spinach and cook for a further couple of minutes or until the spinach has wilted.

SWEET POTATO CAKES AND GARLIC DIP

- 3 sweet potatoes
- 1 tin of sweetcorn
- 2 onions
- Small handful of coriander, chopped
- ¼ tsp cayenne pepper
- 1 tsp cumin
- Good twist of salt and pepper
- 1 large egg
- 150g plain breadcrumbs
- Glug of oil
- 250ml plain yogurt
- 1 clove of garlic

Method

1. Prick the sweet potato and throw in the microwave for 5–10 minutes. Once they have cooled down, slice open and scoop out the flesh into a bowl.
2. Throw the sweetcorn, chopped onion, ¾ of the coriander and all of the spices into the bowl and mix. Then, launch in the egg and breadcrumbs and give a good mix until combined. Cover and put in the fridge for 30 minutes.
3. For the dip, mix the yogurt, the rest of the coriander and minced garlic. Mix. Job done!
4. Heat up a pan and glug in the oil. Form patties from the sweet potato mixture and fry for about 2 minutes on either side until golden brown on each side.

GROW

GREEN PIZZA

- 2 heads of broccoli
- 1 can of artichokes
- 1 jar of green pesto (or use our homemade version from the Prep Recipes chapter)
- 1 lb pizza dough
- Glug of oil
- 1 mozzarella ball, shredded
- Feta, crumbled
- Handful of parmesan, grated

<u>Method</u>

1. Cut broccoli into small florets and bung in a bowl with a lid, drizzle over some water and throw in the microwave for 4 minutes. Drain.
2. Spread oil onto a pan. Place pizza dough on the pan and spread some pesto over it.
3. Sprinkle ¾ of the mozzarella cheese over the pesto, then the broccoli and the artichoke. Finally, sprinkle the remainder of the mozzarella, feta and Parmesan.
4. Bake in the oven for 30 minutes.

GROW

Dan Keeley

Rome to Home campaign

WHAT IS YOUR EXPERIENCE WITH MENTAL ILLNESS?

Five years ago, in 2012, at the age of twenty-seven, I experienced a full-scale manic episode while on holiday in Italy. I spent a few weeks in psychiatric wards in Italy and another couple of weeks in psychiatric units back in the UK. I got a clear diagnosis of bipolar disorder.

From January 2012 until the manic episode in mid-2012, there were some early warning signs. I wasn't sleeping or eating properly. I was constantly on the go. I believed I could change the world and I was trying to come up with ideas on how to do so, with an overwhelming sense of empathy and creative skills.

I went on holiday to Italy with my fiancé, who is now my wife. Building up to the manic episode, I had bought a bottle of wine for every room in the hotel and gave away all my possessions. These series of events led me to believe that I was the chosen one. My fiancé realised that I was unwell, so she called our family to come out and help. She contacted a psychiatric unit an hour away. On the way, my compulsion to change the world for the better escalated. I pulled the car over onto a hard shoulder and started stopping cars on the motorway. I stood in the middle of the motorway, in the middle of rush hour, backing up traffic because I believed I was the one to show the world how to slow down and 'follow their hearts'. I genuinely believed I was sent to help the world to slow down.

The police and ambulance teams arrived and took me to the hospital as soon as they could, pumping me full of drugs to slow me down. I felt confused and in a mess. I went from feeling that I had 100 per cent conviction in every atom of my being, to waking up a week later with 0 per cent conviction in any words that left my lips. I was riddled with anxiety and couldn't trust any aspect of myself. I went from believing I was the chosen one to believing I was the biggest burden on society.

The six months that followed were the darkest time in my life. I was in a desperate and debilitating dark place and did not want to exist anymore. I was pinned to the bed and couldn't even walk the two metres to the sink to brush my teeth. I felt numb and empty. I felt emotionless and the medication didn't work. My body was in shock and I had to start all over again. I couldn't think, move or walk.

So, I had to start changing things, one of which was practising minimalism. I started to strip away life's excess and pressures. I got involved with the minimalist movement, which is all about removing as much of life's excess as possible to create as much capacity as possible to focus on what really matters most – which, in my eyes, were health, relationships, growth, passions and contributing to others. As well as minimalism, I found it was all about talking, trusting the medication, exercising, sleeping well and eating well.

Until 2012, I regularly had fluctuating moods, but it had never been so severe as the episode in Italy. It was a critical time and I count myself extremely lucky for the support I received.

Since 2013, I have been on a steadily progressive journey back to the positive place I find myself in today. In August 2017, I channelled my energy into running 1,250 miles from 'Rome

To Home' (from the Colosseum to the London Eye) in order to share my story and keep men alive by talking about it.

WHAT DO YOU DO TO KEEP YOURSELF ON A STEADY LEVEL?

Being open about my experiences helps me to keep my mood on a positive and stable level. I have an incredibly supportive team around me, who I calls my 'Dream Team' – my family, friends, colleagues and caring associates, who tell me when things seem a little off. I take regular medication and run. Indeed, physical exercise is amazing for me, as it makes me hungry, meaning I eat well, which, in turn, makes me sleep well. Two things that are paramount for those with bipolar disorder are resting and not overstimulating yourself mentally.

My cocktail for keeping myself in a steady place is eating well, sleeping well, exercising, talking and practising minimalism as best I can – continually making as much capacity as possible for looking after my overall health.

WHAT IS YOUR FAVOURITE FOOD?

I can't choose just one meal! The list would include my mum's roast chicken, my wife's prawn risotto and fajitas. However, if I had to choose one for this book, it would be the risotto – full of chorizo, prawns, garlic, Parmesan and white wine.

A B S

Starting in a standard plank position, raise your hips as high as they can go, then lower them back down.

Continue this movement for as long as possible. Make sure your back stays straight and your hips don't droop.

DYNAMIC PRONE PLANK

FLUTTER KICK

Start lying on your back with your arms at your sides and your palms facing down. Keep your legs extended, lift your heels off the floor (about 6 inches). Make quick, small up-and-down pulses with your legs, while keeping your core engaged.

RUSSIAN TWIST

Sit on the floor with your knees bent and feet together, a few inches off the floor. With your back at a 45-degree angle from the ground, move your arms from one side to another in a twisting motion. Here, slow and steady wins the race. The slower the twist, the deeper the burn.

ABS

RAOK

Avoid road rage, honking,
yelling while driving
Let someone go ahead of you in
a queue
Run an errand for a friend
Leave a small gift for the
school secretaries
Hold the door open for someone
Donate colouring books and
crayons to a doctor's surgery
or hospital
Put money in a parking meter
Offer to get someone a drink
from the kitchen or to make
them a snack
Leave nice comments on the
blogs you read regularly
Call your parents or another
family member and catch up

METHOD

1. IN A DUTCH OVEN OR HEAVY LARGE POT, HEAT OLIVE OIL OVER MEDIUM HIGH HEAT. ADD ONION, CELERY, CARROTS, AND GARLIC UNTIL VEGGIES ARE SOFTENED, 1-2 MIN. ADD CHILI POWDER, SMOKED PAPRIKA, SUGAR, ALLSPICE, AND CUMIN. STIR AND COOK 1 MIN. ADD BROTH, LENTILS, AND PASSATA. BRING TO A BOIL AND IMMEDIATELY REDUCE HEAT TO A SIMMER. COVER AND SIMMER 30 MIN.

2. ADD BLACK BEANS, CORN, AND COVER. CONTINUE SIMMER 20 MORE MIN OR UNTIL LENTILS ARE NICELY TENDER AND MIXTURE HAS THICKENED. IF NEEDED, ADD A BIT MORE BROTH TO LOOSEN. ADD SALT AND BLACK PEPPER TO TASTE.

3. SERVE WITH DESIRED TOPPINGS.

LENTIL AND 3 BEAN CHILLI

- **BOWL OF LENTILS**
- **TIN OF BLACK EYED BEANS, KIDNEY BEANS,**
  PINTO BEANS AND SWEET CORN
- **1 ONION**
- **1 CARTON OF PASATA**
- **3 CLOVES OF GARLIC**
- **1 TBSP PAPRIKA, CHILLI POWDER,**
  CUMIN AND ALL SPICE
- **1 PINT OF VEG STOCK**

Dean Merrick

PE Teacher

WHAT IS YOUR EXPERIENCE WITH MENTAL ILLNESS?

When I was ten, I was sexually assaulted by a known person. I never spoke about it. I pushed it to the back of my mind. School was a constant struggle for me and I was constantly negatively compared to my sister. I was told I was a waste of space and my career advisor told me that I was going one of two ways, either prison or work at the industrial estate down the road.

When I turned eighteen, my grandfather, who was a great inspiration to me, died. My grandfather had been in the navy, so I felt inspired to get a trade and I applied to the navy. I was told my eyesight wasn't good enough and the aftermath of being turned down made me experience my first bout of depression. I was nineteen. I was reckless; drinking, smoking and getting into trouble.

When I was twenty, my cousin helped me to get to America to coach football. At the same time, I was studying to become a personal trainer. At this point, I felt my life started to turn around in a professional aspect. After America, I decided I wanted to go to university because I wanted to become a PE teacher. When

I was twenty-four, my mum became ill. She had suffered from alcoholism for many years – something that runs in my family – and basically drank herself to death. I struggled with this, but I had always been a stiff-upper-lip type of person, so I sucked it up and got on with life. I was in a dark place at that time and drank heavily myself. I used to get intrusive dreams, which I had from the age of fifteen years old. I would dream that I had raped or murdered somebody and in the morning, especially after I had been drinking, I wouldn't be able to remember if it was real or a dream. I would sit and wait for the police to turn up. While waiting, I would drink.

I had been good at football when I was younger. I had felt a lot of pressure on me because of my potential. The pressure manifested itself into anxiety, to the point where I didn't want to play football anymore.

I knew I had a problem with alcohol. I could easily drink between 20 to 25 pints of beer on a Sunday session. I knew I needed to get away in order to change. So, I started to go to Powerleage in London and got away from alcohol. The change of scenery did me good. Things went well for a while and I met a girl who became my wife. However, in 2011, my wife became ill with a blood clot and was very sick. Around this time, my grandmother died. I developed panic attacks that built with anger, so any situation that annoyed or angered me, however slightly, would blow up.

In September 2015, I started a job as head of PE and my son was born. I had a new house with my wife. I thought it would be a good job for me, but it had many challenges. I found the first year very difficult and looking back, I can see that I was depressed when I started the job. The signs were that I would sit at home crying, lying on the floor and not doing anything. I didn't want to eat. Around the same time, my friend, Phil, took his life. Phil had been my friend through college. From around the ages of twenty to twenty-five, we had been great friends, playing football and going out together. When I found out about Phil taking his life, I couldn't comprehend what had happened. Then, in 2015, another of my friends took his life by driving into a tree. I felt myself sinking deeper and deeper into depression. My work pressures grew. I tried to hide my depression and took to alcohol again. Things went downhill.

One day, I was in a staff briefing at the school. The teachers were given more work and I spoke up about how I thought the work was pointless. I was kept back after the meeting and, in front of everyone, I broke down. I had uncontrollable tears. The headteacher called the doctor. I was thirty-six when I was formally diagnosed with depression and anxiety. The school wanted me to sign off work, but I didn't want to. I wanted to continue working. I only slept for two hours a night and drank lots of coffee. I was put on sleeping tablets. My next breakdown was in front of the kids at the school. The kids were fantastic, but yet again I was sent home and the school wanted to sign me off. Eventually, they literally barred me from the building. After many anxiety episodes, I was referred to a mental health hospital in Warwick. I wasn't detained, but I had a structured programme with psychotherapists and psychiatrist.

I started to exercise again. I realised through my therapy that I have had many suicidal thoughts throughout my adult life. During my recovery time, I looked after my young son. This helped a lot as I and my family knew I would never do anything to harm myself with my son around me.

I still have dark days and bouts of depression and anxiety. I have found that talking about it and being open has helped me. I feel very much supported by my workplace, my family and my friends. My workplace had shown me immense support. The head of the school has accepted my mental illness and the students have been amazing in helping me.

WHAT DO YOU DO TO KEEP YOURSELF ON A STEADY LEVEL?

I love running! I have always done it, but started again when I was off work. I also take medication. I think I may be on medication for the rest of my life.

WHAT IS YOUR FAVOURITE FOOD?

My favourite food is Chinese lemon chicken and egg fried rice.

NOTES

NOTES

EXERCISE

We are not saying you need to sign up for the next marathon or become an Ironman overnight, but exercise is the best medicine for depression. Choose to walk to the shop instead of drive. Take the stairs at work, instead of the lift. Take your kids to the park with a ball, park in the corner of the supermarket instead of fighting for the 10 spaces next to the door. There are many ways to get those endorphins released. The first step is the hardest, as it is with most things but once you do, the rest of the steps will follow and you will feel better and more motivated.

- **The NHS guidelines for physical activity is at least 150 minutes of moderate aerobic activity such as cycling or brisk walking every week.**
- **Strength exercises on two or more days a week that work all of the major muscles (legs, hips, back, abdomen, chest, shoulders and arms)**

So, breaking that down it's only 21 minutes a day. Everybody should easily be able to do that every day if you put your mind to it. With the 3 workout plans you have in this book and the 20 exercises explained it makes it very easy to be able to do a workout in your own home without any equipment.

All workouts are based on time so in the timescale you must do an exercise it doesn't matter if you do 1 rep or 20 reps within the time if you keep moving and put 100% into it.

Enjoy the workouts and get the kids, friends and family involved and make it 20 mins of fun.

FULL BODY TABATA

Complete all exercises with 20 seconds of work and 10 seconds rest. start with the number 1's then 2's then 3's and so on until every exercise has been completed in the order of Cardio, Upper, Lower then Core. Then Repeat.

CARDIO

UPPER

LOWER

CORE

EMOM WORKOUT

Set a timer for 5 minutes.
Complete the exercises in each round, and rest until the next minute begins. You'll perform the exercises in each round 5 times (starting at the beginning of each minute, for 5 minutes). This entire workout is only 15 MINUTES LONG!

EMOM 5

CV-
LB-
UP-
ABS-

EMOM 5

CV-
LB-
UP-
ABS-

EMOM 5

CV-
LB-
UP-
ABS-

CV- Cardio Vascular, LB- Lower Body
UP - Uper Body, ABS- AB Exercises

8 Minute AMRAP Circuits

Complete all 4 AMRAP circuits or pick and choose ones you want to do based on how much time you have! This workout can be as short as 8 minutes or as long as 32 minutes. Focus on speed, but also ensure you're keeping good form!

CV - Cardio Vascular, LB - Lower Body, UB - Upper Body, ABS - Abdominals

AMRAP #1
- CV - x10
- LB - x10
- UB- x10
- ABS- x10

AMRAP #2
- CV - x10
- LB - x10
- UB- x10
- ABS- x10

AMRAP #3
- CV - x10
- LB - x10
- UB- x10
- ABS- x10

AMRAP #4

Grains

PAsta
Rice
egg noodles
Quinoa
Green Lentils
Sushi Rice
Risotto Rice

Fresh Herbs

Parsley
Coriander
Basil
Mint
Rosemary
Chives

Cheese

Cheddar
Mozzarella
Feta
Parmesan
Halloumi

Frozen

Peas

Other

Nori Sheets
Orange Juice
White Wine

Bread/Baking
Pitta
Wholemeal Flour
Breadcrumbs
Cornflour
Chickpea Flour
Flour

Fruit
Bananas
Limes
Lemons
Blueberries
Oranges

Sauces & Condiments

Oil	Sesame Oil
Mustard	Balsamic Vinegar
Vegetable Stock	Honey
Beef Stock	Curry Paste
Chicken Stock	Worcestershire Sauce
Garlic Paste	Siracha Sauce
Ginger Paste	
Chilli Sauce	
Soy Sauce	
Pepper	

Shopping List

Shopping List 2

Seafood

Cod	Prawns
Salmon	Smoked Salmon

Vegetables

Lettuce	Asparagus	Sweet Potato
Cucumbers	Broccoli	Jalapenos
Tomatoes	Cauliflower	Bean Sprouts
Bell Peppers	Beetroot	Carrots
Sugar Snap Peas	Mushrooms	Parsnip
Celery	Spinach	Leaks
Onions	Potatoes	Red Onion
Garlic	Red Cabbage	New Potato
Butternut Squash	Kale	Shallots
Courgette	Green Beans	

Dairy

Eggs
Cream Cheese
Milk
Greek Yoghurt
Creme Fraiche
Coconut Milk
Almond Milk

Meat

Chicken
Turkey
Pork
Beef
Streaky Bacon
Ham

Herbs & Spices

Salt
Ras el hanout
Garlic
Cardamom Pods
Oregano
Garam Masala
Cinnamon Stick
Chilli Flakes
Bay Leaves
Star Anise

Coriander
Curry Powder
Paprika
Thyme
Cumin
Chilli Powder
Ground Ginger
Turmeric
Allspice
Pepper

Deli Meat

Chorizo

Canned and Packaged Goods

Pinto Beans
Black Beans
Kidney Beans
Tomatoes
Sweetcorn

Artichoke
Olives
Passata
Chickpea

MY SHOPPING LIST 📋

Recommended Websites, Blogs and Stories

Websites:

WWW.MENTALHEALTH.ORG.UK

WWW.CLASPCHARITY.COM

WWW.TIME-TO-CHANGE.ORG.UK

WWW.MIND.ORG.UK

WWW.HEADSTOGETHER.ORG.UK

WWW.SAMARITANS.ORG

Blogs and Stories:

WWW.RICHBISCUIT.COM

WWW.ROMETOHOME.COM

WWW.THESTRANGERONTHEBRIDGE.COM

WWW.JONNYBENJAMIN.CO.UK

Do **YOU** want exclusive recipes, tips on how to prepare food, hints on what you can do to **HELP** your **MENTAL HEALTH**, workout ideas and cooking videos?

Go to

WWW.TMTBOOK.CO.UK

and **SUBSCRIBE** to the exclusive members club.